The Open University

MST326 Mathematical methods and fluid mechanics

Block 4

The cover image is of a two-dimensional Kármán vortex street (courtesy of the Institute of Computational Fluid Dynamics, Tokyo, Japan).

This publication forms part of an Open University course. Details of this and other Open University courses can be obtained from the Student Registration and Enquiry Service, The Open University, PO Box 197, Milton Keynes MK7 6BJ, United Kingdom: tel. +44 (0)845 300 6090, email general-enquiries@open.ac.uk

Alternatively, you may visit the Open University website at http://www.open.ac.uk where you can learn more about the wide range of courses and packs offered at all levels by The Open University.

To purchase a selection of Open University course materials visit http://www.ouw.co.uk, or contact Open University Worldwide, Walton Hall, Milton Keynes MK7 6AA, United Kingdom, for a brochure: tel. +44 (0)1908 858793, fax +44 (0)1908 858787, email ouw-customer-services@open.ac.uk

The Open University, Walton Hall, Milton Keynes, MK7 6AA.

First published 2009.

Edited, designed and typeset by The Open University, using the Open University TₑX System.

Printed and bound in the United Kingdom by Cambrian Printers Limited, Aberystwyth.

ISBN 978 0 7492 2845 3

1.1

Contents

UNIT 12   Water waves

Study guide

This unit refers back particularly to *Unit 9* Section 5, dealing with the basics of wave motion, and to the treatment of Laplace's equation and the velocity potential function in *Unit 11*. However, some reference is also made to *Units 5* and *6*.

Section 3 of this unit uses the hyperbolic functions sinh, cosh and tanh. The first two were also used in *Unit 11*, but if you need a reminder about the properties of these functions, see *Unit 2* Appendix 1 and Subsection 4.2 of the *Handbook*.

Section 5 is very short, while Sections 1–4 may take roughly equal times to study.

There is an audio session associated with Section 3.

Introduction

Unit 9 Subsection 5.2 introduced some of the basic concepts associated with wave motion. We introduced wave parameters such as wavelength, period, wave speed and amplitude, and discussed the propagation of waves on strings. The analysis of finite-length strings in *Unit 10* demonstrated the possibility of standing waves. Water motion can also exhibit each of these phenomena, though not usually in such a well-defined manner as string waves.

Water waves are the subject of this unit. You are probably familiar with waves on water; perhaps you have meditated on the waves coming inexorably onto a beach, or perhaps, on a summer's afternoon, you have watched waves spreading out over a lake. On a trip across the Channel, you may have seen longer rolling waves on a deep sea, or you will have heard of the havoc caused by tidal waves, such as the tsunami that hit countries around the Indian Ocean in late 2004. In fact, all of these waves fall into the general class of *gravity waves*, and it is such waves that are the subject of this unit. Although these waves are maintained by the force of gravity, they may be initiated by the tide, by a stone thrown into a pond, by the wind or by an earthquake beneath the sea. The waves are visible as a surface wave disturbance; however, the presence of a wave can be detected by pressure variations to a depth of at least a wavelength, as will be seen later in this unit.

These waves are called gravity waves because they are driven by a balance between the fluid's inertia and its tendency to return to the equilibrium state under gravity.

Section 1 describes two examples of real water waves, which introduce some of the features that will be modelled. Then a *linearised model* of water waves is developed, in which it is assumed that the squares and products of velocity components are so small as to be negligible.

Real waves can be complicated phenomena, with waves of many different wavelengths and amplitudes present. To make a start, Sections 2 and 3 model the water motion by waves of one wavelength at a time. Section 4 discusses the effect of combining two (sinusoidal) waves whose wavelengths differ slightly from one another.

Finally, Section 5 presents an explanation for a familiar physical situation.

Wave parameters

The following wave parameters, and their relationships to *angular frequency* ω and *scaled wave number* $k = 2\pi\kappa$, are used throughout this unit. (Here κ is the (unscaled) *wave number*, which is the number of complete waves in unit length.)

For further details, see *Unit 9* Subsection 5.2.

wavelength (length of one complete wave)
$$\lambda = \frac{2\pi}{k} = \frac{1}{\kappa}$$

period (time taken for one complete wave to pass any fixed point)
$$\tau = \frac{2\pi}{\omega}$$

frequency (number of waves passing a fixed point in unit time)
$$f = \frac{\omega}{2\pi} = \frac{1}{\tau}$$

wave speed (distance travelled by the wave in unit time)
$$c = \frac{\lambda}{\tau} = \frac{\omega}{k} = \frac{f}{\kappa} = f\lambda$$

Note also that, throughout this unit, the wave *amplitude* is assumed to be small compared to the wavelength. Take $g = 9.81\,\mathrm{m\,s^{-2}}$.

1   Modelling water waves

This section discusses some types of physically occurring waves, and formulates a mathematical model which is fundamental to a basic theory of water waves. The extent of the problem can be seen by comparing the photograph of the apparently erratic nature of a water surface shown in Figure 1.1 with the simple sinusoidal wave model in Figure 1.2.

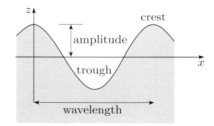

Figure 1.1

Figure 1.2

A connecting link between the model and reality is provided by *Unit 10*, where the idea of a Fourier series representing a function as a sum of sine and cosine functions was introduced. By superposing a series of simple sinusoidal waves of increasing frequency, a complicated wave profile can be constructed. This provides a strong incentive to study sinusoidal wave solutions. On the other hand, waves on a water surface are sometimes found with shapes that look like a sine wave.

Subsection 1.1 begins by describing the formation of real water waves in two familiar situations. Then we start to model water waves, by attempting to represent some of their identifiable features mathematically.

1.1 Water waves in nature

Formation of water waves at sea

Most water waves are formed as a result of changes in the pressure and velocity of the air in close proximity to the water surface, although some of the largest water waves are caused by tides, earthquakes and major water movements due to currents and the Earth's rotation.

The process of wave formation is not fully understood, but higher-speed winds are certainly associated with higher mean wave heights, as shown by the empirical results in Table 1.1.

Wave height is the difference between the heights of a crest and an adjacent trough.

Table 1.1   Effect of wind speed on mean wave height

Beaufort number	Wind speed $(\mathrm{m\,s^{-1}})$	Air description 10 m above sea	Water description	Mean wave height (m)
1	1	light air	rippled sea	0.2
2	3	slight breeze	wavelets	0.5
3	5	gentle breeze	slight sea	1.25
4	8	moderate breeze	moderate sea	3
5	11	fresh breeze	quite rough	4.25
6	15	strong breeze	very rough	6
7	18	moderate gale	high sea	7.5
8	22	fresh gale		8.5
9	26	strong gale	very high sea	11.5
10	30	whole gale		13
11	35	storm		14
12	38	hurricane		15+

The Beaufort wind force scale was created in 1805 by Admiral Sir Francis Beaufort (1774–1857).

The simplest theory of wind-generated waves shows that, once started, a wave will be increased in amplitude by a wind blowing in the same direction as the wave motion. Assuming that the wind exerts pressure mainly on the windward slopes of water, it follows, for example, that the wind pressure on the water between B and C in Figure 1.3 will be greater than it will be on the slope AB. The wind increases the water movement in the wave and so transfers energy to it, the wind being slowed down a little in the process. The wind will cause waves travelling in the same direction to grow, while waves travelling in the opposite direction will be reduced.

Such a wave is initially caused by viscous forces at the water surface.

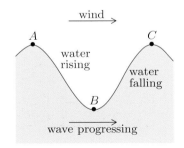

This simple theory would provide stimulus only to waves travelling at a slower speed c than the wind speed w, and generally the amount of energy added to the wave would depend on the relative speed, $w - c$. These results agree generally with observation.

Figure 1.3

It can be observed that shorter-wavelength waves travel more slowly than longer-wavelength waves, and that they can obtain energy more quickly from a favourable wind. Also, these waves are more liable to break and so dissipate their energy into turbulence and foam. However, waves of longer wavelength can absorb and retain more wind energy, and these waves tend to predominate, at least in the long term. Data in a UK Admiralty manual support this conclusion. This manual gives typical North Atlantic waves as having a period of 7 seconds, a wavelength of over 70 m and speed $10\,\mathrm{m\,s^{-1}}$, with waves occasionally reaching up to 200 m long at speeds of $17\,\mathrm{m\,s^{-1}}$. In the South Pacific, waves over 300 m long travelling at $25\,\mathrm{m\,s^{-1}}$ are more the norm. The longer waves in the South Pacific are due to the longer 'fetch' (the distance over which waves can develop without impediment).

It is generally assumed that small disturbances of the water surface are started through changes in air pressure and air velocity at the water surface; after this start, a wind can take over and build up the water disturbance, generally increasing the wavelength so that more and more energy is transferred to the wave motion. Attenuation due to the water's viscosity has been calculated to have a significant effect only after the wave has travelled around the Earth two or three times; this form of wave attenuation can therefore be ignored, since a land mass will usually have been encountered before then. So long-wavelength waves, once generated by strong or storm winds, can continue over long stretches of the ocean, perhaps increased by favourable winds or attenuated by contrary winds. For example, a storm in the South Atlantic can generate waves which reach the British Isles several days later.

Attenuation means a reduction in the energy carried by the wave.

In studying these sea waves experimentally, the following feature of waves on deep water becomes apparent. Although waves of many wavelengths are generated by a storm, the longer-wavelength waves reach our coast before those of shorter wavelength, suggesting that

> the wave speed is an increasing function of wavelength.

Observation 1

Waves whose speed depends on the wavelength are said to be *dispersive*.

More is said about dispersive waves in Section 3.

Pebble dropped into a pond

A pebble dropped into water has an effect which is similar to a localised storm at sea, but on a much smaller scale. Waves of various wavelengths are initiated at the impact point, and these propagate away in circles, with the longer-wavelength waves overtaking any shorter-wavelength waves which may have been created earlier. The circular wave propagation is illustrated in the photograph of such waves shown in Figure 1.4.

Figure 1.4

As the pebble enters the pond, it pushes aside the water as shown in Figure 1.5(a), causing a disturbance to the water surface, which moves away from the pebble. As time goes on, the water below the pebble is pushed up around the pebble into the space occupied by the pebble in Figure 1.5(a). The increased pressure below the pebble causes this. The water surface is now even more disturbed, as shown in Figure 1.5(b). Further, less violent, disturbances emanate from the pebble's descent as time goes on. The disturbance (e.g. that in Figure 1.5(b)) can be taken to consist of a Fourier sum of waves of many different wavelengths, just like any other irregular water surface disturbance. These waves are again dispersive, because the speed of propagation of any such wave increases as the wavelength increases; this means that the longer-wavelength waves, travelling faster, sooner or later move ahead of the shorter-wavelength waves, and the initial disturbance breaks up into groups of waves of approximately equal wavelengths. As time goes on, these waves become more drawn out and their amplitudes decrease owing to the initial energy being spread out over a widening circle. The attenuation of the waves owing to viscosity in the water is very small indeed.

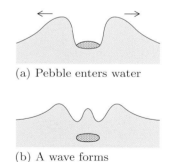

(a) Pebble enters water

(b) A wave forms

Figure 1.5

Watching a leaf (or small stick) on a water surface shows that there is no large-scale movement of the water as waves pass by. The leaf bobs up and down and oscillates back and forth around an equilibrium position. Very close observation shows that the leaf is describing a circular path if the water is 'deep'. Figure 1.6 illustrates this feature very clearly in a laboratory situation, where waves have been generated on the surface of water in a long tank. The motion of the fluid particles is inferred from that of neutrally buoyant solid particles. Figure 1.6 shows that

What 'deep' means here is defined in Sections 2 and 3.

A neutrally buoyant solid particle has the same density as the surrounding fluid.

Observation 2

> for waves in deep water, the fluid particles describe circles whose radii decrease with depth.

Any useful model of waves in deep water, no matter how simple, should agree with these observed features:

Observation 1:   wave speed is an increasing function of wavelength;

Observation 2:   the fluid particles describe circles whose radii decrease with depth.

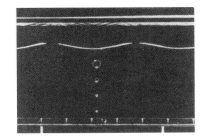

Figure 1.6   Circular particle paths

1.2   Basic assumptions and equations

Subsection 1.1 discussed means of generating waves at sea and on a pond, and the surface features of real waves. The observed wave patterns are very complicated and are made up of many individual waves of different wavelengths and speeds. The surface profile is forever changing with time, so that attempting to model this water motion is challenging.

As in all modelling, it is best to investigate a rather idealised physical problem first, and see whether the observations identified in Subsection 1.1 are predicted by this model. Consider a long rectangular channel, containing water to an equilibrium depth h. Suppose that waves can propagate through the water in this channel (see Figure 1.7) with the surface oscillating about an equilibrium level.

The analysis will consider the propagation of harmonic waves on the water surface which are uniform across the channel (in the y-direction). Such waves could be produced by vibrating a paddle in the x-direction at one end of the tank, but the method of wave generation is of no concern here. Cartesian coordinate axes are chosen as shown in Figure 1.7, with the z-axis vertically upwards and the x-axis in the direction of the wave motion; the plane $z = 0$ is the equilibrium level of the water surface. Since the waves are uniform across the channel, the wave profiles are independent of y. The physical situation can therefore be considered in just the (x, z)-plane, as shown for one instant of time in Figure 1.8.

Harmonic (sinusoidal) waves were introduced in *Unit 9* Subsection 5.2.

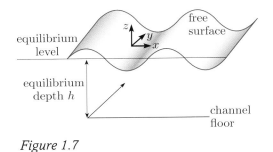

Figure 1.7

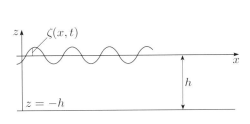

Figure 1.8

To describe the free surface of the water at any point x and time t, we introduce a function ζ, so that the free surface profile has the equation

$$z = \zeta(x, t).$$

At any instant of time, $t = t_1$ say, the graph of the function $\zeta(x, t_1)$ shows the surface profile at that time. The function ζ is called the **surface profile function**.

We begin with the following assumptions about the nature of water and of the body force.

1. Water is inviscid and has constant density, ρ say.
2. The only body force is that due to gravity (which is conservative).

The inviscid and constant-density assumptions should be familiar to you by now, and provide a good model for water away from any solid boundaries. The inviscid assumption requires some care. In discussing the generation of sea waves by the wind in Subsection 1.1, it was suggested that surface waves are caused by the action of viscous forces at the air/water interface. Although a viscous model is required to set the waves in motion, it is no longer needed when considering the established waves.

Now consider the following assumptions for the flow.

3. For a wave motion, the flow is *unsteady*. (This means that the surface displacement $\zeta(x_1, t)$ at each fixed position x_1 is a function of t.)
4. The flow is *irrotational*.

Further assumptions, about the type of waves to be considered, are as follows.

5. This analysis will use a *linearised theory of waves* in which the velocity components (and their derivatives) are regarded as so small that their squares and products may be neglected.
6. The amplitude of the waves is small relative to their wavelength, from which it follows that $\partial\zeta/\partial x$, the slope of the surface profile, is also small. (Hence the products of ζ, $\partial\zeta/\partial x$ and any velocity component may also be ignored.)
7. Surface tension is ignored. (Surface tension is important only for waves of relatively small wavelength.)
8. Fluid particles which are initially *in* the free surface stay in the surface as it moves. (This assumption is based on experimental evidence.)

Other analyses of wave motion retain these second-order terms and derive models for waves of finite amplitude.

The assumptions may appear to be very restrictive. However, they lead to mathematical models that describe real features surprisingly well, provided that the models are applied appropriately.

It is possible to show that the surface profile function $\zeta(x, t)$ satisfies the one-dimensional wave equation

$$\frac{\partial^2 \zeta}{\partial t^2} = c^2 \frac{\partial^2 \zeta}{\partial x^2}.$$

However, the derivation is rather involved, and a different approach is possible. We first formulate the equations of motion in terms of the velocity potential ϕ (which exists because the flow is irrotational, by Assumption 4, so that $\mathbf{curl\,u} = \mathbf{0}$), and then we satisfy the boundary conditions at the free surface and at the channel floor. Finally we express ζ in terms of ϕ.

Consider the main body of water, the free surface and the channel floor in turn.

(i)   The main body of water

From Assumption 4, the flow is irrotational, and so we can define a velocity potential $\phi(x, z, t)$ such that

$$\mathbf{u} = \nabla\phi.$$

The constant-density model (Assumption 1) implies that the continuity equation takes the form

$$\nabla \cdot \mathbf{u} = \nabla^2\phi = 0 \qquad (-h < z < \zeta(x, t)),$$

so that ϕ satisfies Laplace's equation throughout the fluid and for all values of t.

Unless stated otherwise, throughout this unit, the ranges $-\infty < x < \infty$ and $t > 0$ are associated with each partial differential equation.

(ii)   The free surface

Fluid particles initially *in* the free surface stay in the surface as it moves (Assumption 8). Consider a fluid particle in the free surface whose position at time t is given by $x = x(t)$, $z = z(t)$. (See Figure 1.9, which shows the positions A_1 and A_2 of such a particle at times t_1 and t_2.)

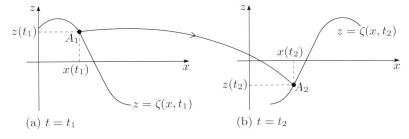

(a) $t = t_1$ (b) $t = t_2$

Figure 1.9   Particles stay in the surface

There are three conditions at the free surface, although only two are independent.

(a)   At any instant of time t, the vertical component of the velocity of a fluid particle is

$$u_3 = \frac{dz}{dt}.$$

Now, for a particle in the free surface, we have $z = \zeta(x, t)$, by Assumption 8, so that

$$(u_3)_{z=\zeta} = \frac{d\zeta}{dt}(x, t)$$

$$= \left(\frac{\partial}{\partial t} + \mathbf{u} \cdot \nabla\right)\zeta(x, t)$$

$$= \frac{\partial\zeta}{\partial t} + (u_1)_{z=\zeta}\frac{\partial\zeta}{\partial x}.$$

Using Assumption 6, the second term on the right-hand side may be ignored as negligibly small, and so, to first order,

$$(u_3)_{z=\zeta} = \frac{\partial\zeta}{\partial t}. \tag{1.1}$$

Here, 'to first order' means that terms involving powers and products of quantities deemed 'small' are ignored.

This equation says that, to first order, the local upward velocity of the surface, $\partial\zeta/\partial t$, is equal to the fluid particle velocity component u_3 at the surface.

(b)   To derive a second free surface condition, consider Bernoulli's equation in the form

$$\frac{p}{\rho} + \tfrac{1}{2}u^2 + gz + \frac{\partial \phi_1}{\partial t} - f(t) = \text{constant along any curve,}$$

See *Unit 6* Subsection 1.3.

where for convenience the velocity potential is written as ϕ_1. Here we have used the fact that the only body force is due to gravity (Assumption 2).

Unit 11 showed that the velocity potential function is unique only to within an additive constant. However, here ϕ_1 is time-dependent, and $\mathbf{grad}(\phi_1) = \mathbf{grad}(\phi_1 + F(t))$ for any function F; that is, ϕ_1 is unique only to within an additive arbitrary function of t. So we write

Unit 11 did not consider time-dependent velocity potentials.

$$\phi = \phi_1 - \int f(t)\,dt,$$

and then Bernoulli's equation becomes

$$\frac{p}{\rho} + \frac{\partial \phi}{\partial t} + gz + \tfrac{1}{2}u^2 = \text{constant along any curve.}$$

The constant on the right-hand side can be assigned any value, by suitable adjustment to the potential function ϕ; take this value to be p_0/ρ. The equation can then be written as

$$\frac{\partial \phi}{\partial t} + gz + \tfrac{1}{2}u^2 = \frac{p_0 - p}{\rho}.$$

This equation can also be used to give the pressure at any point below the free surface.

At any time t, the pressure p at the free surface ($z = \zeta$) is atmospheric pressure, so that

$$\left(\frac{\partial \phi}{\partial t}\right)_{z=\zeta} + g\,\zeta + \tfrac{1}{2}(u^2)_{z=\zeta} = 0.$$

Ignoring the second-order term $\tfrac{1}{2}(u^2)_{z=\zeta}$, by Assumption 5, we have

$$\left(\frac{\partial \phi}{\partial t}\right)_{z=\zeta} + g\,\zeta = 0. \tag{1.2}$$

This surface condition on ϕ at $z = \zeta$ can be simplified by using the Taylor expansion for ϕ at $z = 0$, giving

$$(\phi)_{z=\zeta} = (\phi)_{z=0} + \zeta \left(\frac{\partial \phi}{\partial z}\right)_{z=0} + O(\zeta^2).$$

Here $(\phi)_{z=0} = \phi(x, 0, t)$.

(Recall that $O(\zeta^2)$ means terms of second and higher order in ζ.)

The maximum value of ζ is its amplitude, and $\partial \phi/\partial z$ is the velocity component u_3. Thus ζ and $(\partial \phi/\partial z)_{z=0}$ are first-order terms, and so Assumption 6 gives, to first order,

Since $\mathbf{u} = \boldsymbol{\nabla}\phi$, we have $u_3 = \partial \phi/\partial z$.

$$(\phi)_{z=\zeta} = (\phi)_{z=0}, \qquad \text{that is,} \qquad \phi(x, \zeta, t) = \phi(x, 0, t).$$

Hence also $(\partial \phi/\partial t)_{z=\zeta} = (\partial \phi/\partial t)_{z=0}$; the surface condition (1.2) then becomes, to first order,

$$\left(\frac{\partial \phi}{\partial t}\right)_{z=0} + g\,\zeta = 0. \tag{1.3}$$

Similarly, the Taylor expansion of u_3 in Equation (1.1) about $z = 0$ gives

$$(u_3)_{z=\zeta} = (u_3)_{z=0} + O(\zeta\,\partial u_3/\partial z, \; \zeta^2).$$

Hence this surface condition becomes, to first order,

$$(u_3)_{z=0} = \frac{\partial \zeta}{\partial t}. \tag{1.4}$$

Exercise 1.1

In the derivation above, the pressure at the free surface ($z = \zeta$) is assumed to be atmospheric. Waves also occur at the interface of two liquids in which a lighter liquid forms a layer above a denser one (see Figure 1.10). If ϕ_1 and ϕ_2 are the velocity potential functions in each fluid, and ρ_1 and ρ_2 are the densities, find the surface boundary condition at the interface which is equivalent to Equation (1.3) above.

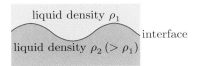

Figure 1.10

(c)   The third free surface condition is obtained by eliminating ζ between Equations (1.3) and (1.4). Differentiating Equation (1.3) with respect to t gives

$$\frac{\partial}{\partial t}\left(\left(\frac{\partial \phi}{\partial t}\right)_{z=0}\right) + g\frac{\partial \zeta}{\partial t} = 0, \tag{1.5}$$

and, substituting for $\partial \zeta / \partial t$ from Equation (1.4) in Equation (1.5), this gives

$$\left(\frac{\partial^2 \phi}{\partial t^2}\right)_{z=0} + g(u_3)_{z=0} = 0.$$

From the definition of ϕ, we have

$$(u_3)_{z=0} = \left(\frac{\partial \phi}{\partial z}\right)_{z=0},$$

Note that $\mathbf{u} = \boldsymbol{\nabla}\phi$.

leading to

$$\frac{\partial^2 \phi}{\partial t^2} + g\frac{\partial \phi}{\partial z} = 0 \quad \text{at } z = 0. \tag{1.6}$$

This surface condition turns out to be the most convenient to use. As said above, the analysis of water waves is carried out in terms of ϕ. This velocity potential satisfies Laplace's equation ($\nabla^2 \phi = 0$) within the fluid, and at the free surface ϕ satisfies Equation (1.6). Note that this condition applies at $z = 0$.

The conditions at the channel floor are somewhat easier to write down.

(iii)   The channel floor

The inviscid model is being used here, and so the normal boundary condition applies; at the (solid) channel floor this is

See *Unit 5* Subsection 2.3.

$$\mathbf{u} \cdot \mathbf{n} = u_3 = 0 \quad \text{at } z = -h.$$

Here $\mathbf{n} = \mathbf{k}$.

In terms of the velocity potential, this becomes

$$\frac{\partial \phi}{\partial z} = 0 \quad \text{at } z = -h.$$

13

We are now in a position to summarise the findings so far. From the preceding analysis, the mathematical problem to be solved is as follows:

Linearised wave model

For gravity water waves, with small amplitude relative to wavelength, the velocity potential $\phi(x, z, t)$ satisfies the equations

$$\frac{\partial^2 \phi}{\partial x^2} + \frac{\partial^2 \phi}{\partial z^2} = 0 \qquad (-h < z < 0), \tag{1.7a}$$

Each of these equations holds for $-\infty < x < \infty$ and $t > 0$.

$$\frac{\partial^2 \phi}{\partial t^2} + g \frac{\partial \phi}{\partial z} = 0 \qquad \text{at } z = 0, \tag{1.7b}$$

This was Equation (1.6).

$$\frac{\partial \phi}{\partial z} = 0 \qquad \text{at } z = -h. \tag{1.7c}$$

These equations can be solved for the potential function ϕ. However, waves are observed by seeing the movement of fluid particles on the surface. Although it is the surface profile, $\zeta(x, t)$, that is sought, it is more convenient to work with ϕ and Equations (1.7). (It is possible to detect the waves *within* the fluid by the pressure changes.) Equation (1.3) provides the link between ζ and ϕ, expressed as follows:

Surface profile function

The relationship between the surface profile function $\zeta(x, t)$ and the velocity potential $\phi(x, z, t)$ is

$$\zeta = -\frac{1}{g} \left(\frac{\partial \phi}{\partial t} \right)_{z=0}. \tag{1.8}$$

Exercise 1.2

If $\phi = D \cosh\left(k(z + h)\right) \cos(kx - \omega t)$, find the equation of the shape of the free surface. What is the amplitude of ζ in terms of the constants in ϕ?

This formula for a velocity potential ϕ is derived in Section 3.

The derivation of these equations uses several mathematical simplifications. These simplifications hinge on Assumptions 5 and 6, which depend on the amplitude of the surface waves being small compared to the wavelength. These assumptions permit the neglect of second- and higher-order terms in Equations (1.7b) and (1.8).

Exercise 1.3

Classify the following statements as true or false.

(a) The surface profile is given by the graph of the function ϕ.

(b) Both ϕ and ζ satisfy Laplace's equation.

(c) The waves can be detected only at the surface.

(d) In the linearised theory, the amplitude of ζ is small relative to the wavelength.

1.3 Progressive wave solution

Seeking a general solution of Equations (1.7), governing gravity water waves, would be very difficult. The approach here will be to find a solution that models a harmonic progressive wave. On the surface, waves can be represented by sine and cosine functions, and such waves were discussed in some detail in *Unit 9*. A more general waveform can be built up in terms of these harmonic waves by using Fourier analysis, so that the approach here does have further value.

At any instant of time, a harmonic wave travelling in the positive x-direction on a free surface will have the profile shown in Figure 1.11.

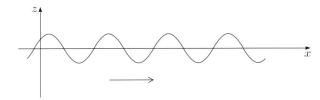

Figure 1.11   Harmonic wave progressing in the positive x-direction

The equation for this profile is

$$z = \zeta(x, t) = a \sin(kx - \omega t),$$

where a is the amplitude, ω is the angular frequency and $\lambda = 2\pi/k$ is the wavelength; a, ω and k are constants. The analysis of Subsection 1.2 has assumed $a \ll 2\pi/k$. Now, the equations to be solved are given in terms of the potential function, ϕ. Equation (1.8), which provides the link between ϕ and ζ, gives in this case

$$\left(\frac{\partial \phi}{\partial t} \right)_{z=0} = -g\,\zeta = -ag \sin(kx - \omega t). \tag{1.9}$$

Equation (1.7a) says that ϕ is a solution of Laplace's equation. In *Unit 11* solutions of Laplace's equation were found using the method of separation of variables, and such an approach gives ϕ in the form $\phi = X(x)\,Z(z)$, where X and Z are trigonometric, hyperbolic or exponential functions. In the current situation, ϕ depends on t as well as on x and z; however, for a progressive wave, the dependence on x and t has a special form, with the term $x - ct$ introduced to embody the progressive nature of the wave. Thus we take

$$\phi(x, z, t) = X(x - ct)\,Z(z).$$

This form for ϕ satisfies Laplace's equation provided that

$$\frac{X''(x - ct)}{X(x - ct)} = -\frac{Z''(z)}{Z(z)}.$$

Since ϕ must satisfy Equation (1.9), the form for X will necessarily be in terms of the trigonometric functions sine and cosine. It is justified then to assume that ϕ has the form

$$\phi(x, z, t) = Z(z) \cos(kx - \omega t). \tag{1.10}$$

Sine or cosine could be used here, but for convenience sine is chosen.

Here, for example, X'' denotes the second derivative of X, a function of one variable.

Here

$$X(x - ct) = \cos(kx - \omega t),$$

where $c = \omega/k$.

Exercise 1.4

Show that, with a suitable choice for $Z(0)$, the potential function given by Equation (1.10) satisfies Equation (1.9).

Substituting ϕ from Equation (1.10) into Laplace's equation will give a differential equation for $Z(z)$. The steps in the above development, i.e. starting with Equation (1.8), provide a justification for writing ϕ as in Equation (1.10) for a progressive wave travelling in the x-direction, and the following approach is now adopted:

(a) assume ϕ to be given by Equation (1.10);

(b) find $Z(z)$ from Laplace's equation (1.7a);

(c) impose the surface and channel floor conditions, (1.7b) and (1.7c), and hence specify ϕ;

(d) use Equation (1.8) to obtain the surface profile ζ (once ϕ is known).

Steps (c) and (d) are the subject of Sections 2 and 3, which investigate waves on infinitely deep water (in Section 2) and on water of finite depth (in Section 3). The following exercise asks you to tackle Step (b).

Exercise 1.5

Starting with

$$\phi(x, z, t) = Z(z)\cos(kx - \omega t),$$

find the functional form of Z for which ϕ satisfies Laplace's equation (1.7a).

The solution for $Z(z)$ is written in two ways in Solution 1.5:

(a) in terms of exponential functions, as

$$Z(z) = Ae^{-kz} + Be^{kz};$$

(b) in terms of hyperbolic functions, as

$$Z(z) = D\cosh\left(k(z+h)\right) + E\sinh\left(k(z+h)\right).$$

These solutions are equivalent, since we can put
$$A = \tfrac{1}{2}(D - E)e^{-kh},$$
$$B = \tfrac{1}{2}(D + E)e^{kh}.$$

Which form is more useful depends on the location of the boundary at $z = -h$. In Section 2, where $h = \infty$, it is convenient to take solution (a), whereas in Section 3, for finite h, solution (b) is more convenient.

Finally, note that the surface condition (1.7b),

$$\frac{\partial^2 \phi}{\partial t^2} + g\frac{\partial \phi}{\partial z} = 0 \quad \text{at } z = 0,$$

will give a relationship between k and ω which *must* be satisfied. This is the *wave condition* since, as explained in Sections 2 and 3, this condition leads to an expression for the wave speed in terms of the wavelength.

This condition is found for each of the cases considered in Sections 2 and 3.

To summarise, for a harmonic progressive wave travelling in the x-direction, the velocity potential function is

$$\phi(x, z, t) = (Ae^{-kz} + Be^{kz})\cos(kx - \omega t),$$

or equivalently,

$$\phi(x, z, t) = [D\cosh\left(k(z+h)\right) + E\sinh\left(k(z+h)\right)]\cos(kx - \omega t).$$

The theory developed in this section has assumed that the amplitude of the surface wave profile is small relative to the wavelength, and has therefore neglected the square of the particle speed in Bernoulli's equation in comparison with the gravity terms. Also, the second-order terms in Taylor expansions have been neglected. Such an approach leads to waves called *linearised gravity waves*.

End-of-section exercises

Exercise 1.6

A harmonic wave is propagating in the x-direction and has period $2\,\text{s}$, wavelength $4\,\text{m}$ and amplitude $0.1\,\text{m}$. Write down an equation defining the shape of the surface profile. Find the form of the velocity potential function ϕ, given that $\lim_{z \to -\infty} \phi = 0$.

Exercise 1.7

Consider the velocity potential function

$$\phi(x, z, t) = 0.05 \cosh\left(\pi(z + 0.1)\right) \cos\left(\pi(x - 6t)\right).$$

What are the values of the wave number, the wavelength, the wave speed and the period for this wave?

Find the equation of the surface profile function ζ, and hence find its amplitude.

See page 6 for the relationships between wave parameters.

2 Deep water gravity waves

In Section 1 you saw that the function

$$\phi(x, z, t) = (Ae^{-kz} + Be^{kz})\cos(kx - \omega t), \tag{2.1}$$

where A and B are arbitrary constants, satisfies Laplace's equation and is a possible velocity potential function for gravity waves travelling in the positive x-direction. The values of A and B are determined from the conditions at the free surface and at the channel floor.

This section investigates waves on deep water. We model 'deep water' by choosing the depth to be infinite. However, in Section 3 you will see that the solution derived here also applies to finite depths greater than half the wavelength of the wave, and so the rather idealised solution in this section is also relevant to finite-depth situations.

2.1 Solution for infinite depth

We start with the boundary conditions given by Equations (1.7b) and (1.7c).

Exercise 2.1

Write down the two boundary conditions on the velocity potential when modelling gravity waves on water of infinite depth.

The solution to this exercise provides two equations which the velocity potential function given by Equation (2.1) must satisfy. Consider first the condition at the channel floor:

$$\lim_{z \to -\infty} \frac{\partial \phi}{\partial z} = 0.$$

From Equation (2.1), we have

$$\frac{\partial \phi}{\partial z} = k(-Ae^{-kz} + Be^{kz}) \cos(kx - \omega t),$$

and for this to be zero in the limit as $z \to -\infty$, for all values of x and for all positive t, we must choose $A = 0$. Hence

$$\phi(x, z, t) = Be^{kz} \cos(kx - \omega t). \tag{2.2}$$

Now, at the free surface the condition to be met is

$$\frac{\partial^2 \phi}{\partial t^2} + g\frac{\partial \phi}{\partial z} = 0 \quad \text{at } z = 0. \tag{2.3}$$

Substituting for ϕ from Equation (2.2) into the left-hand side of Equation (2.3), we have

$$\frac{\partial^2 \phi}{\partial t^2} + g\frac{\partial \phi}{\partial z} = -B\omega^2 e^{kz} \cos(kx - \omega t) + gkBe^{kz} \cos(kx - \omega t)$$

$$= (-\omega^2 + gk)Be^{kz} \cos(kx - \omega t).$$

Thus the free surface condition (2.3) becomes

$$(-\omega^2 + gk)B \cos(kx - \omega t) = 0 \qquad (-\infty < x < \infty, \; t > 0).$$

Except in the trivial case where $B = 0$ (and hence $\phi = 0$), we must have

$$\omega^2 = gk. \tag{2.4}$$

This equation, known as the **wave condition** for deep water waves, provides a necessary relationship between ω and k for the velocity potential function ϕ in Equation (2.2).

Example 2.1

Find a velocity potential function for a deep water gravity wave with a period of 8 seconds. What is the wave speed for this function?

Solution

From Equations (2.2) and (2.4), we have

$$\phi(x, z, t) = Be^{kz} \cos(kx - \omega t),$$

where B is constant and $\omega^2 = gk$.

Since the period is 8 seconds, we obtain

$$\omega = \frac{2\pi}{\tau} = \frac{2\pi}{8} = \tfrac{1}{4}\pi = 0.785\,\mathrm{s}^{-1} \quad \text{(to 3 significant figures)}.$$

Using Equation (2.4), we have

$$k = \frac{\omega^2}{g} = \frac{\pi^2}{16g} = 0.0629\,\mathrm{m}^{-1} \quad \text{(to 3 significant figures)}.$$

The velocity potential function for this wave is therefore

$$\phi(x, z, t) = Be^{0.0629z} \cos(0.0629x - 0.785t).$$

The wave speed is

$$c = \frac{\omega}{k} = \frac{4g}{\pi} = 12.5\,\mathrm{m\,s}^{-1} \quad \text{(to 3 significant figures).} \quad \blacksquare$$

Exercise 2.2

Find the velocity potential function for a deep water gravity wave with a period of $\frac{1}{4}$ second. What are the values (to 3 significant figures) of the wave speed, wavelength and amplitude of this potential function?

It is apparent from the solutions to this example and exercise that the surface amplitude B of the potential function is independent of period and wavelength, although it must be 'small' relative to the wavelength in order that the derivation of the equations of water wave theory in Subsection 1.2 is valid. From the solution to Exercise 2.2, it is clear now that, with the exception of this amplitude, all the wave parameters for deep water gravity waves can be expressed in terms of just one parameter. In Exercise 2.2 the given parameter was τ, the period of the wave. Clearly, the period is easily measured: it is the time difference between the arrivals of consecutive wave crests at any fixed point. Another quantity that can be measured easily is the wavelength: it is the distance between two adjacent crests at a given instant.

In Example 2.1 and Exercise 2.2, the period was given. In the following exercise, a given wavelength is the starting point.

Exercise 2.3

A deep water gravity wave has wavelength 10 m. Find a velocity potential function for this wave. What are the period and speed of this wave?

In the next exercise, you are asked to derive an expression for the surface profile from the expression for the potential function.

Exercise 2.4

Find the equation of the surface profile $z = \zeta(x, t)$ for an 'infinite-depth' gravity wave. What is the relationship between the amplitude a of ζ and the surface $(z = 0)$ amplitude of ϕ?

The solution to this exercise shows that we can describe the surface profile, i.e. 'what we see', in terms of the parameters of ϕ. This justifies the approach of working completely with ϕ and extracting the relevant information from the properties of ϕ.

The following table lists the *measurable* wave parameters c and τ which have been calculated (as in Exercise 2.3) for different wavelengths, together with suggested classifications in terms of types of sea waves that may be familiar to you.

Table 2.1   Classification of deep water gravity waves

λ, wavelength (m)	0.01	0.1	1	10	100	1000
c, wave speed (m s^{-1})	0.12	0.40	1.2	4.0	12	40
τ, period (s)	0.080	0.25	0.80	2.5	8.0	25
classification	small ripple	large ripple	beach wave	swell	long rollers	very long rollers

Table 2.1 illustrates the fact that the wave speed, c, depends on the wavelength, λ; in fact, c is a function of λ only, as we shall now show. The wave speed and wavelength are related to ω and k by the formulas $c = \omega/k$ and $\lambda = 2\pi/k$, respectively. Hence

$$c^2 = \frac{\omega^2}{k^2}$$

$$= \frac{gk}{k^2} \quad \text{(by Equation (2.4))}$$

$$= \frac{\lambda g}{2\pi} \quad \text{(since } \lambda = 2\pi/k\text{)}.$$

This formula relates the speed of a harmonic wave, c, and its wavelength, λ. The longer the wavelength, the faster the wave travels. This property of deep water waves is not seen in many other types of waves. For example, light and sound waves travel at speeds independent of their wavelength; in water (pure, at 20°C), all sound waves travel with speed 1482 m s^{-1}.

The relationship between c and λ,

$$c = \left(\frac{\lambda g}{2\pi}\right)^{1/2},$$

is an increasing function, and thus a wave of wavelength λ_1, say, will travel faster than all waves of shorter wavelength ($\lambda < \lambda_1$). An immediate consequence of this is that any one deep water wave continually overtakes those of shorter wavelength, and is itself continually overtaken by waves of longer wavelength. In particular, when the crest of a wave catches up with the crest of a slower wave (of shorter wavelength), the crests reinforce each other, leading momentarily to a higher crest.

The above relationship between c and λ explains (in the context of the infinite-depth model) Observation 1 of Subsection 1.1.

On the surface of the sea, or on a lake, waves of many wavelengths may be generated. Since these individual waves travel at different speeds, the actual wave profile visible on the surface will change its shape as it propagates across the water surface. Only a 'pure' harmonic wave of one wavelength can propagate without a change of shape; however, such waves are relatively rare in nature. We return to the subject of combinations of waves of different wavelengths in Section 4.

Here c and τ are given correct to 2 significant figures.

Typically, long waves in the Atlantic have wavelengths of about 200 m, whereas in the Pacific they are about 350 m in wavelength.

The word 'swell' denotes waves that have travelled a long distance from the storm that formed them, and have become stable and regular.

This formula, together with $\tau = \lambda/c$, can be used to check the entries in Table 2.1.

As you will see in Section 3, waves with different wavelengths on very shallow water all travel with the same speed.

See page 9.

To summarise the results so far:

Waves in deep water

For the model of waves propagating in the positive x-direction in infinitely deep water, the velocity potential function is

$$\phi(x, z, t) = B e^{kz} \cos(kx - \omega t), \qquad \text{where} \qquad \omega^2 = gk.$$

The wave speed c and wavelength λ are related by

$$c^2 = \frac{\lambda g}{2\pi}.$$

The surface profile function is

$$\zeta(x, t) = -a \sin(kx - \omega t), \qquad \text{where} \qquad a = \frac{B\omega}{g} = \frac{Bk}{\omega} = \frac{B}{c}.$$

It is assumed that $B > 0$ and $a > 0$.

Exercise 2.5

A seaman on the deep Pacific Ocean reports seeing a gigantic wave with wavelength twice as long as the ship and with a period of 2 minutes. Can he be believed? Give a reason for your answer.

Exercise 2.6

Surface waves are passing a $10\,\text{m}$ long boat every $4\,\text{s}$, with a wavelength just equal to the boat's length. What is the speed of the boat, if the direction of its motion is the same as that of the wave's motion?

2.2 Particle paths

Subsection 1.1 discussed features of water wave motion. It was observed that small, neutrally buoyant particles, suspended in deep water in wave motion, travel in circles, with radii that decrease with depth. We are now in a position to validate the mathematical theory for deep water waves (as developed in Subsection 2.1) by showing that it predicts such circular particle paths.

See Observation 2 on page 9.

As before, take the potential function for a gravity wave on water of infinite depth to be

$$\phi(x, z, t) = B e^{kz} \cos(kx - \omega t), \qquad \text{where} \qquad \omega^2 = gk.$$

To derive the pathlines we use Procedure 1.1 from *Unit 5*. In Cartesian coordinates, the equations of the pathlines are

$$u_1 = \frac{dx}{dt} \qquad \text{and} \qquad u_3 = \frac{dz}{dt},$$

where $\mathbf{u} = u_1\,\mathbf{i} + u_3\,\mathbf{k}$. Since $\mathbf{u} = \mathbf{grad}\,\phi$, we have

$$\frac{dx}{dt} = u_1 = \frac{\partial \phi}{\partial x} = -kB\,e^{kz} \sin(kx - \omega t) \tag{2.5}$$

and

$$\frac{dz}{dt} = u_3 = \frac{\partial \phi}{\partial z} = kB\,e^{kz} \cos(kx - \omega t). \tag{2.6}$$

In Procedure 1.1 of *Unit 5*, the two-dimensional velocity field is $\mathbf{u} = u_1\,\mathbf{i} + u_2\,\mathbf{j}$ and the motion is independent of z. Here, u_3 takes on the role of u_2 and the motion is independent of y.

This pair of simultaneous, first-order, non-linear differential equations cannot be solved exactly by analytical methods. We have to make some assumptions and approximations in order to proceed.

We assume that at some time t, the position (x, z) of a fluid particle is given as a small displacement from an equilibrium position, (x_0, z_0), by

$$x = x_0 + X \quad \text{and} \quad z = z_0 + Z,$$

where X and Z are small.

The assumption is reasonable given the observations concerning the motion of a leaf on a pond (see page 9).

Substituting for x and z in Equations (2.5) and (2.6) gives

$$\frac{dX}{dt} = -kB\,e^{k(z_0+Z)}\sin(kx_0 + kX - \omega t) \tag{2.7}$$

and

$$\frac{dZ}{dt} = kB\,e^{k(z_0+Z)}\cos(kx_0 + kX - \omega t). \tag{2.8}$$

If we expand the right-hand side of Equation (2.7) using a Taylor series about the point given by $(X, Z) = (0, 0)$, we obtain

The Taylor series is for a function of two variables, X and Z.

$$\frac{dX}{dt} = -kB\,e^{kz_0}\sin(kx_0 - \omega t) - k^2 B\,e^{kz_0}\cos(kx_0 - \omega t)\,X$$
$$- k^2 B\,e^{kz_0}\sin(kx_0 - \omega t)\,Z + kB \times O(k^2 X^2, k^2 XZ, k^2 Z^2). \tag{2.9}$$

We now argue that the second and third terms on the right-hand side here may be ignored in comparison with the first. From Assumption 6 on page 10, the amplitude a of the surface waves is small relative to their wavelength, λ; that is, $a \ll \lambda$. Since the vertical motion of particles cannot depart from equilibrium further than indicated by this amplitude, we have $|Z| \leq a$. Since also $\lambda = 2\pi/k$, it follows that

$$k|Z| \leq ka \ll k\lambda = 2\pi, \quad \text{that is,} \quad k|Z| \ll O(1).$$

Hence the term of Equation (2.9) involving $k^2 BZ$ is much smaller than the term involving kB, and may be discounted.

The corresponding argument for the term involving $k^2 BX$ follows in a similar way, after establishing that $|X| \leq a\pi$. This is deduced after noting from Equation (2.7) that $|dX/dt| \leq kB$. Now $kB = a\omega$ (from Exercise 2.4), and so over half a period of the surface wave we have

Note that $z_0 \leq 0$, so that $e^{kz_0} \leq 1$.

Since $kB = a\omega$, we have

$$|X| \leq a\omega \times \frac{\pi}{\omega} = a\pi.$$

$$kB = \left(\frac{a}{\lambda}\right)\omega\lambda = 2\pi c\left(\frac{a}{\lambda}\right),$$

The upshot of this is that only the first term on the right-hand side of Equation (2.9) need be retained, and so, to first order,

so that the first term on the right-hand side of Equation (2.9) is $O(a/\lambda)$. The next two terms are $O((a/\lambda)^2)$, and so on.

$$\frac{dX}{dt} = -kBe^{kz_0}\sin(kx_0 - \omega t). \tag{2.10}$$

By a similar analysis we can expand the right-hand side of Equation (2.8), and, neglecting all but the first term, we obtain, to first order,

$$\frac{dZ}{dt} = kBe^{kz_0}\cos(kx_0 - \omega t). \tag{2.11}$$

Integrating Equations (2.10) and (2.11) gives the parametric form of the particle pathline. We have

The constants of integration are taken to be zero in each case; this is done because $(X, Z) = (0, 0)$ represents the equilibrium position of the particle.

$$X = -\frac{kB}{\omega}e^{kz_0}\cos(kx_0 - \omega t), \quad Z = -\frac{kB}{\omega}e^{kz_0}\sin(kx_0 - \omega t).$$

Since $kB = a\omega$, this is equivalent to

$$X = -ae^{kz_0}\cos(kx_0 - \omega t), \quad Z = -ae^{kz_0}\sin(kx_0 - \omega t). \tag{2.12}$$

Eliminating t between these parametric equations, we obtain

$$X^2 + Z^2 = a^2 e^{2kz_0}.$$

This is the equation of a circle of radius ae^{kz_0} and centre $(X, Z) = (0, 0)$, which corresponds to the point (x_0, z_0). Thus the infinite-depth gravity wave solution gives circular pathlines whose radii decrease with depth. Figure 2.1 shows some of these pathlines.

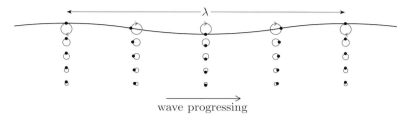

Figure 2.1   Circular particle paths (model)

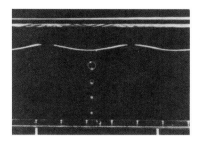

Figure 2.2   Circular particle paths (in the laboratory)

The features of the pathlines in this figure agree qualitatively with the experimental observations described in Subsection 1.1 and reproduced in Figure 2.2. Furthermore, from Equations (2.12) we see that a fluid particle takes $2\pi/\omega$ seconds to complete one journey around its circular path, and this is the period of the surface wave profile. Thus a particle at a crest at some instant t_1 and position x_1 will arrive back at the top of its circular pathline at the instant the next crest arrives.

From Equations (2.10), (2.11) and (2.12), we have

$$\frac{dX}{dt} = \omega Z, \quad \frac{dZ}{dt} = -\omega X,$$

from which it can be deduced (for this right-moving wave, with $\omega > 0$) that the particle paths are traversed clockwise, as shown in Figure 2.1.

Exercise 2.7

(a) Show that at a depth of half a (surface) wavelength (i.e. at $z_0 = -\frac{1}{2}\lambda$), the radius of the circular path is less than 5% of its surface value (for $z_0 = 0$).

(b) Show that, at a given depth (z_0 fixed), the radius of the particle path will be smaller for a surface wave of the same amplitude but higher frequency.

The result of Exercise 2.7(a) allows us to relax our meaning of 'deep' as being 'infinite in depth'. At a depth of half a wavelength, the fluid particles are displaced from the centre of their circular paths by about 4% of the displacement of those at the surface. Further, most of the physical quantities associated with water waves depend on ϕ, and since the z-variation of ϕ is given by e^{kz}, at a depth of half a wavelength the amplitude of ϕ, which is Be^{kz}, is also about 4% of its surface value. Thus we could take the deep water theory of this section to apply to water whose depth is greater than or equal to half a wavelength. We shall return to this interpretation of 'deep' in Section 3, and give a further justification for this choice.

In this section we have investigated gravity waves on very deep water. We began the analysis by assuming water of infinite depth, but the results of this subsection suggest that the theory may apply to finite depths greater than or equal to one half of the wavelength of the wave being discussed. The theory has given two results agreeing with previous observations:

(i) waves of different wavelengths travel with different speeds;

(ii) the fluid particle paths are circles whose radii decrease with depth.

Another interesting feature of the model is that it has no parameter to indicate that the liquid on which waves propagate is water, since inviscid flow was assumed from the outset, and the density, ρ, was eliminated during the arguments used to set up the model. Hence the results

A laboratory demonstration and animation of such particle paths can be found via Section 2 of the *Media Guide*. This also validates the prediction of Exercise 2.7(b).

developed here also apply to any other liquid with a free surface and air or another gas above, provided that the flow can be assumed to be inviscid.

In reality, this 'deep' water (gravity) wave theory models a variety of waves from small ripples a few centimetres in wavelength on 'not too shallow' ponds to very long sea waves such as Atlantic rollers with wavelengths of around 600 m, speeds of around $30\,\mathrm{m\,s^{-1}}$ and periods of around 20 s. These long sea waves are often generated by a storm at sea, and the longest-wavelength waves reach our coast first, giving warning of the storm to come. For example, the long waves can travel 2500 km across the Atlantic in a day, whereas the storm may take several days to arrive (and indeed may not reach our coast at all). However, the very-long-wavelength waves caused by volcanic action, earthquakes or tides have wavelengths over 1000 m. Where the ocean depth is less than half of a wavelength, for example over the continental shelf, an alternative theory is needed because such waves cannot be modelled as deep water waves, even though the ocean may seem 'deep' in comparison to its surroundings. This is the subject of Section 3.

> This relies on the density of the gas being negligible compared with that of the liquid. For waves at an interface between two liquids, the ratio of the densities is a significant factor; see Exercise 1.1.

Stokes drift

Despite the prediction of circular particle paths being apparently validated by experimental observations, you should remember that this prediction is based on a linearised model. When non-linearities are taken into account, it turns out that there is a small drift velocity for particles, superimposed on the main circular motion and in the direction of wave propagation. In fact, if the expressions for X and Z in Equations (2.12) are fed back into the X and Z terms in Equation (2.9), with higher-order terms still being neglected, it is found that Equation (2.10) is replaced by

> There is no need to check this calculation.

$$\frac{dX}{dt} = -kBe^{kz_0}\sin(kx_0 - \omega t) + \frac{k^3 B^2}{\omega}e^{2kz_0}.$$

Since $kB = a\omega$, $\omega = ck$ and $k = 2\pi/\lambda$, the drift velocity in the direction of wave motion has magnitude

> To the same order, Equation (2.11) for dZ/dt is unchanged.

$$\frac{k^3 B^2}{\omega}e^{2kz_0} = \omega k a^2 e^{2kz_0} = 4\pi^2 c \left(\frac{a}{\lambda}\right)^2 e^{2kz_0}.$$

This is of second order in the ratio a/λ, whereas (from Equations (2.10) and (2.11)) particles are predicted to traverse the circular paths in the linearised model at a speed of $kBe^{kz_0} = 2\pi c(a/\lambda)e^{kz_0}$. This effect, known as *Stokes drift*, is therefore difficult to detect when a/λ is small. It also diminishes rapidly with depth.

> George Stokes derived an expression for this drift in 1847.

The geometric effect is to replace closed circular pathlines, predicted by the linearised theory, by a succession of loops that gradually advance in the direction of wave progression, as shown in Figure 2.3.

End-of-section exercises

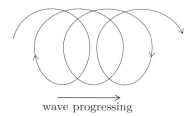

wave progressing

Figure 2.3

Exercise 2.8

Waves caused by a stationary storm at sea are measured by a distant weather station to have a wavelength of 8 m at 06:00 on Monday. By 18:00 on the same day, the wavelengths are down to $1\frac{1}{2}$ m. Find the distance of the storm from the station and the time at which the storm started, assuming that the deep water theory applies and that the waves leave the storm at the same time and travel with their respective single wave speeds.

Exercise 2.9

A gravity wave of period 2.5 s is propagating in deep water. Calculate the wavelength and speed of the wave, and write down the velocity potential function for the case where the surface profile has amplitude $\frac{1}{2}$ m. How deep must the water be for the 'deep water' wave model to apply?

Describe the pathlines of the fluid particles at the surface and at depths of 0.1λ, 0.5λ and 2λ, where λ is the wavelength.

3   Waves in water of finite depth (audio)

We now investigate gravity waves in water with finite depth h. The method of attack is similar to that in Section 2 for 'infinite-depth' waves, i.e. we shall again seek solutions to Equations (1.7) on page 14. Since the analysis is similar to that of Subsection 2.1, you are asked to do much of the work as exercises in the audio session for this unit. We begin by finding exact solutions that apply for all depths. Then we recover the deep water solution of Section 2, and introduce the idea of shallow water waves.

The results of the following exercise, relating to the hyperbolic tangent function, tanh, will be useful in the audio session.

If you need a reminder about hyperbolic functions, see *Unit 2* Appendix 1 and Subsection 4.2 of the *Handbook*.

Exercise 3.1

(a) Show that
$$\lim_{x \to \infty} \tanh(kx) = 1,$$
where k is a positive constant.

(b) Determine the first two non-zero terms of the Taylor series expansion about $x = 0$ of the function
$$f(x) = \tanh x.$$
Hence show that
$$\lim_{x \to 0} \left(\frac{\tanh x}{x} \right) = 1.$$

When you are ready, start the audio at Track 31 of CD2.

1   Deep water waves — the mathematical problem

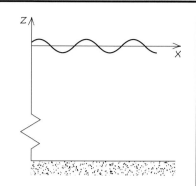

In the fluid:
$$\frac{\partial^2 \phi}{\partial x^2} + \frac{\partial^2 \phi}{\partial z^2} = 0 \qquad (-\infty < z < 0). \qquad (1a)$$

At the surface:
$$\frac{\partial^2 \phi}{\partial t^2} + g\frac{\partial \phi}{\partial z} = 0 \qquad \text{at } z = 0. \qquad (1b)$$

At the channel floor:
$$\lim_{z \to -\infty} \frac{\partial \phi}{\partial z} = 0. \qquad (1c)$$

2   Deep water waves — solution

Velocity potential: $\phi(x, z, t) = Be^{kz} \cos(kx - \omega t).$

Wave condition: $\omega^2 = gk.$

Surface profile: $\zeta(x, t) = -\dfrac{1}{g}\left(\dfrac{\partial \phi}{\partial t}\right)_{z=0} = -\dfrac{B\omega}{g}\sin(kx - \omega t).$

Wave parameters

wave number $\kappa = k/(2\pi),$ wavelength $\lambda = 2\pi/k,$

period $\tau = 2\pi/\omega,$ frequency $f = \omega/(2\pi) = 1/\tau,$

wave speed $c_\infty = \omega/k = f\lambda = \sqrt{\lambda g/(2\pi)}.$

3   Finite-depth water waves — the mathematical problem

We formulate the mathematical problem for waves on water
of finite depth h.

In the fluid:
$$\frac{\partial^2 \phi}{\partial x^2} + \frac{\partial^2 \phi}{\partial z^2} = 0 \qquad (-h < z < 0). \qquad (2a)$$

At the surface:
$$\frac{\partial^2 \phi}{\partial t^2} + g\frac{\partial \phi}{\partial z} = 0 \qquad \text{at } z = 0. \qquad (2b)$$

At the channel floor:
$$\frac{\partial \phi}{\partial z} = 0 \qquad \text{at } z = -h. \qquad (2c)$$

4   Finite-depth water waves — velocity potential

See Exercise 1.5

The velocity potential for the finite-depth water wave
which satisfies Equation (2a) is

$$\phi(x, z, t) = \left[D\cosh\left(k(z + h)\right) + E\sinh\left(k(z + h)\right)\right]\cos(kx - \omega t).$$

5   **Finite-depth water waves — the wave condition and surface profile**

Equation (2c) eliminates one unknown constant:

$$\left(\frac{\partial\phi}{\partial z}\right)_{z=-h} = \boxed{} = 0 \quad \Rightarrow$$

$$\phi(x, z, t) = \boxed{}$$

one unknown constant

Equation (2b) gives the wave condition:

$$\left(\frac{\partial^2\phi}{\partial t^2} + g\frac{\partial\phi}{\partial z}\right)_{z=0} = \boxed{} = 0.$$

Hence the wave condition is

$$\omega^2 = \boxed{}$$

ω as a function of k

Find the surface profile (see Frame 2).

6   **Wave parameters for the finite-depth solution**

Choose λ (the wavelength) to be the one independent parameter and write the following in terms of λ (and h):

scaled
wave number, $k = \boxed{}$ $\omega^2 = \boxed{}$

$\tau^2 = \boxed{}$ $f^2 = \boxed{}$

$c^2 = \boxed{}$ $\displaystyle\lim_{h/\lambda\to\infty} c = \boxed{}$

5A   **The solution with wave condition**

$$\left(\frac{\partial \phi}{\partial z}\right)_{z=-h} = k\left[D\sinh 0 + E\cosh 0\right]\cos(kx - \omega t) = 0 \qquad (3)$$

Since $\sinh 0 = 0$ and $\cosh 0 = 1$, we have $E = 0$.

The velocity potential is then

$$\phi(x, z, t) = D\cosh\left(k(z + h)\right)\cos(kx - \omega t). \qquad (4)$$

From Equation (4),

$$\left(\frac{\partial^2 \phi}{\partial t^2} + g\frac{\partial \phi}{\partial z}\right)_{z=0} = \left(-\omega^2 D\cosh(kh) + gk\,D\sinh(kh)\right)\cos(kx - \omega t) = 0.$$

Hence the wave condition is

$$\omega^2 = gk\tanh(kh). \qquad (5)$$

The surface profile is

$$\zeta(x, t) = -\frac{1}{g}\left(\frac{\partial \phi}{\partial t}\right)_{z=0} = -\frac{D\omega}{g}\cosh(kh)\sin(kx - \omega t).$$

6A   **Wave parameters for finite-depth waves**

$$k = \frac{2\pi}{\lambda}, \qquad \omega^2 = \frac{2\pi g}{\lambda}\tanh\left(\frac{2\pi h}{\lambda}\right),$$

$$\tau^2 = \frac{2\pi\lambda}{g}\coth\left(\frac{2\pi h}{\lambda}\right), \qquad f^2 = \frac{g}{2\pi\lambda}\tanh\left(\frac{2\pi h}{\lambda}\right)$$

$$\text{and} \quad c^2 = \frac{g\lambda}{2\pi}\tanh\left(\frac{2\pi h}{\lambda}\right). \quad \text{Note:} \quad \lim_{h/\lambda \to \infty} c = \sqrt{\frac{g\lambda}{2\pi}} = c_\infty.$$

---

7   **What is meant by 'deep'?**

Let $R = \dfrac{c}{c_\infty}$. Then $R = \sqrt{\tanh\left(\dfrac{2\pi h}{\lambda}\right)}$ (from Frame 6A).

Fill in the following table for the indicated values of h/λ.
Express your calculations correct to 3 decimal places.

h/λ	10	1.0	0.5	0.25	0.1	0.01
R^2						
R						

What can you say about R when $h/\lambda > 0.5$?

7A   **The table of $R = c/c_\infty$ for the given values of h/λ**

h/λ	10	1.0	0.5	0.25	0.1	0.01
R^2	1.000	1.000	0.996	0.917	0.557	0.063
R	1.000	1.000	0.998	0.958	0.746	0.250

The wave speed c is within 0.2% of the 'infinite depth' wave speed c_∞ for $h/\lambda \geq 0.5$. In this case, the water depth is more than half a wavelength. This is our criterion for the deep water wave solution to be valid.

8   **What is meant by 'shallow'?**

For waves on finite-depth water, $c^2 = \dfrac{g\lambda}{2\pi} \tanh\left(\dfrac{2\pi h}{\lambda}\right)$ (see Frame 6A).

Define $c_0 = \lim\limits_{h/\lambda \to 0} c$, and show that $c_0^2 = gh$.

Hint: Let $\alpha = \dfrac{h}{\lambda}$. Then $\dfrac{c^2}{gh} = \dfrac{1}{2\pi\alpha}\tanh(2\pi\alpha)$.

Use Exercise 3.1(b).

- -

Let s be defined by $s = c/c_0$. Fill in the following table for the indicated values of h/λ. Express your calculations correct to 3 decimal places.

h/λ	0.001	0.01	0.02	0.04	0.05	0.06	0.08	0.10	0.20
s									

What can you say about the ratio s for values of $h/\lambda < 0.05$?

8A   **Shallow water wave definition**

The table of $s = c/c_0$ for the given values of h/λ follows:

h/λ	0.001	0.01	0.02	0.04	0.05	0.06	0.08	0.10	0.20
s	1.000	0.999	0.997	0.990	0.984	0.977	0.961	0.941	0.823

The wave speed c is within 2% of $c_0 = \sqrt{gh}$ for $h/\lambda \leq 0.05$.

In this case, the water depth is less than one twentieth of a wavelength.

For very shallow water ($h/\lambda \leq 0.05$), the wave speed is approximated by

$$c_0 = \sqrt{gh}$$

(and c_0 is independent of wavelength).

9   **Summary**

Finite-depth waves   (exact solution)

$$c^2 = \frac{g\lambda}{2\pi} \tanh\left(\frac{2\pi h}{\lambda}\right)$$

holds for all h/λ; used in practice for $0.5 > h/\lambda > 0.05$.

$$\phi(x, z, t) = D \cosh\left(k(z + h)\right) \cos(kx - \omega t)$$

$$\omega^2 = gk \tanh(kh)$$

Shallow waves: $h/\lambda \leq 0.05$

$$c_0^2 = gh$$

 non-dispersive

Deep waves: $h/\lambda \geq 0.5$

$$c_\infty^2 = \frac{g\lambda}{2\pi}$$

dispersive

The results from the audio session are summarised as follows.

Waves in water of finite depth

For the model of waves propagating in the positive x-direction in water of finite depth, the velocity potential function is

$$\phi(x, z, t) = D \cosh\left(k(z+h)\right) \cos(kx - \omega t), \qquad \text{where}$$
$$\omega^2 = gk \tanh(kh).$$

See Frame 5A.

The wave speed, c, and wavelength, λ, are related by

$$c^2 = \frac{\lambda g}{2\pi} \tanh\left(\frac{2\pi h}{\lambda}\right),$$

See Frame 6A.

which may be approximated by $c_0^2 = gh$ for shallow water ($h/\lambda \leq \frac{1}{20}$) and by $c_\infty^2 = \lambda g/(2\pi)$ for deep water ($h/\lambda \geq \frac{1}{2}$).

See Frame 9.

The surface profile function is

$$\zeta(x, t) = -a \sin(kx - \omega t), \qquad \text{where}$$
$$a = \frac{D\omega}{g} \cosh(kh) = \frac{Dk}{\omega} \sinh(kh).$$

The last expression follows from the wave condition. It is assumed that $D > 0$, $a > 0$.

Exercise 3.2

Waves of wavelength 4 m are propagating on water in four rivers, which have depths of 0.1 m, 0.3 m, 1.9 m and 10 m.

For each case, decide whether the wave should be modelled by the deep water, exact or shallow water approximation, and use the appropriate formula to find the wave speed.

Exercise 3.3

A tidal wave crossing a part of the Pacific Ocean where the depth is 5 km has a wavelength of 50 km. Is it appropriate to use the deep water wave model in this case? Find the wave speed, angular frequency and period for this wave, and hence write down the velocity potential function. Find the equation of the surface profile. Can you say anything about the surface amplitude of this wave?

Except for waves on very shallow water (i.e. those for which $h/\lambda \leq 0.05$), the wave speed depends on the wavelength. Figure 3.1 shows a graph of the dimensionless wave speed $c/\sqrt{gh}$ against the ratio λ/h for a fixed depth h. The deep and shallow water wave regions are indicated.

Since λ/h is used here, rather than h/λ as before, we have 'shallow' waves for $\lambda/h \geq 20$ and 'deep' waves for $\lambda/h \leq 2$.

This graph needs to be modified considerably if surface tension effects are included (for small λ), but these are not discussed here.

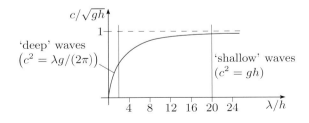

Figure 3.1

The ratio $Fr = u/\sqrt{gh}$, the *Froude number*, was introduced in *Unit 6*; for open channel flow with speed u, the value $Fr = 1$ separates the regimes of subcritical ($Fr < 1$) and supercritical ($Fr > 1$) flows.

See *Unit 6* Subsection 3.1.

If the flow is supercritical, we have $u > \sqrt{gh}$, so that attempting to propagate shallow water waves upstream will fail, as stated in *Unit 6*. We now have an interpretation of the term $\sqrt{gh}$, which was introduced rather arbitrarily in *Unit 6*. The Froude number is the ratio of the speed u of a channel flow to the speed $\sqrt{gh}$ of shallow waves that can be propagated on the water surface in the channel. (Of course, the shallow wave model can only be used to describe waves with wavelength greater than about 20 times the depth. However, as Figure 3.1 illustrates, 'shallow' waves travel faster than other waves, for a given h, and so $\sqrt{gh}$ is an upper limit on all water wave speeds.)

Deep water waves provide examples of dispersive waves, for which the speed varies with the wavelength. Shallow water waves propagate without dispersion (waves of all wavelengths having the same speed). The reason for the name 'dispersive' can be illustrated by considering the propagation of the disturbance shown in Figure 3.2. This is called a 'pulse' and has a narrow width.

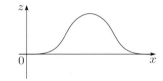

Figure 3.2   A pulse

The theory developed in this unit is for sinusoidal waves; however, we can obtain a waveform of the pulse type shown in Figure 3.2 by combining sinusoidal waves of different wavelengths (i.e. by finding its Fourier series). Now, for such a wave on *shallow* water, the individual sinusoidal waves will all travel at the same speed $\sqrt{gh}$, so that the waveform will not change shape as it travels over the surface. However, for the deep water model, where the wave speed is $\sqrt{\lambda g/(2\pi)}$, the longer-wavelength waves travel faster, leaving the shorter-wavelength waves behind. The waveform will accordingly change shape, and the pulse will be broadened or dispersed in the subsequent motion. The same effect can be expected for other non-sinusoidal waveforms.

For a non-periodic wave, it is more appropriate to use a Fourier transform (MS324 Block I *Chapter 3*) than a Fourier series, though the principle of combining sinusoidal waves is the same.

Exercise 3.4

A wave propagating in the x-direction is formed from the superposition of the two simple waves shown in Figures 3.3(a) and (b). The combined wave is shown in Figure 3.3(c). If the wave propagates in water of depth $0.01\,\text{m}$, describe the subsequent motion and shape of the wave.

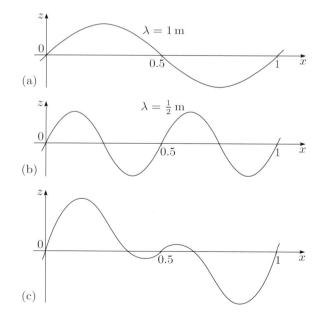

Figure 3.3

For fixed angular frequency ω, the wave speed c decreases as the depth h decreases. This can be seen by rearranging the exact model's equation for c, namely

$$c^2 = \frac{\lambda g}{2\pi} \tanh\left(\frac{2\pi h}{\lambda}\right).$$

See Frame 6A.

Since $\lambda/(2\pi) = 1/k = c/\omega$, this becomes

$$c^2 = \frac{gc}{\omega} \tanh\left(\frac{\omega h}{c}\right),$$

so that

$$c = \frac{g}{\omega} \tanh\left(\frac{\omega h}{c}\right). \tag{3.1}$$

Equation (3.1) shows that c behaves like g/ω for large h (since $\tanh x \to 1$ as $x \to \infty$); for small enough h, on the other hand, c behaves like $\sqrt{gh}$. Both these features are shown in Figure 3.4, which gives the graph of c against h for fixed ω.

If h is small then $\tanh(\omega h/c) \simeq \omega h/c$ and so $c \simeq gh/c$, that is, $c \simeq \sqrt{gh}$.

Equation (3.1) gives c implicitly as a function of h, if ω is fixed. Figure 3.4 is the graph of this function $c(h)$, obtained by solving Equation (3.1) for c, for each value of h.

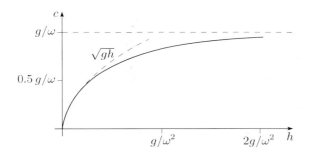

Figure 3.4

Finally in this section, you are asked to find the equations of the particle paths for a finite-depth wave. The method of approach is the same as for 'deep' water waves in Subsection 2.2, as outlined in the following exercise.

Exercise 3.5

The velocity potential function for waves in water of depth h is given by

$$\phi(x, z, t) = D \cosh\left(k(z + h)\right) \cos(kx - \omega t).$$

(a) Write down the corresponding differential equations describing the pathlines of fluid particles.

(b) Consider the path of a particle whose small displacement from an equilibrium position (x_0, z_0) is given by $x = x_0 + X$, $z = z_0 + Z$. By expanding the expressions for dX/dt and dY/dt about the point $(X, Z) = (0, 0)$, show that the differential equations in part (a) reduce to

$$\frac{dX}{dt} = -kD \cosh\left(k(z_0 + h)\right) \sin(kx_0 - \omega t),$$

$$\frac{dZ}{dt} = kD \sinh\left(k(z_0 + h)\right) \cos(kx_0 - \omega t),$$

to first order. (Assume that kD, kX and kZ are small quantities of the same order, so that products of them can be neglected.)

(c) By integrating these equations and then eliminating t, show that the particle paths are ellipses with semi-axes

$$\frac{kD}{\omega}\cosh\left(k(z_0+h)\right) \qquad \text{and} \qquad \frac{kD}{\omega}\sinh\left(k(z_0+h)\right).$$

In Exercise 3.5, you showed that the pathlines are ellipses. Figure 3.5 shows some of these ellipses for a sinusoidal wave travelling from left to right. Much as for the deep water wave case in Subsection 2.2, it can be shown that these particle paths are traversed clockwise for a right-moving wave.

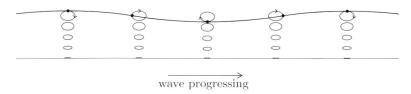

wave progressing

Figure 3.5   Elliptic particle paths (model)

The ellipses become flatter with increased depth, and the axes are shorter. Letting $z_0 \to -h$, we obtain the channel floor paths: the horizontal (semi-major) axis tends to kD/ω and the vertical (semi-minor) axis tends to zero. Thus the model predicts that fluid particles on the channel bed describe simple harmonic motion, with equation

$$x = x_0 - \frac{kD}{\omega}\cos(kx_0 - \omega t), \qquad z = -h.$$

In the inviscid model there is no tangential boundary condition, and so u_1 is not prescribed there. In reality the fluid on the channel bed does not move, so that $u_1 = 0$ as well as $u_3 = 0$ when $z = -h$. This is achieved by rapid variation of u_1 within a narrow boundary layer.

These predictions of elliptic pathlines which become flatter with depth agree qualitatively with experiment. Figure 3.6 shows a photograph of the motion of neutrally buoyant particles suspended in water in a channel. Waves are propagating in this channel from left to right. Once again, the theory describes the features that are observed.

A laboratory demonstration of such particle paths can be found via Section 2 of the *Media Guide*.

As in Subsection 2.2, a small Stokes drift is predicted when non-linear terms are taken into account.

Figure 3.6   Elliptic particle paths (in the laboratory)

End-of-section exercise

Exercise 3.6

A wave propagating in the x-direction is formed from the superposition of the two simple waves shown in Figures 3.7(a) and (b). The combined wave is sketched in Figure 3.7(c) by adding the displacements of the individual waveforms.

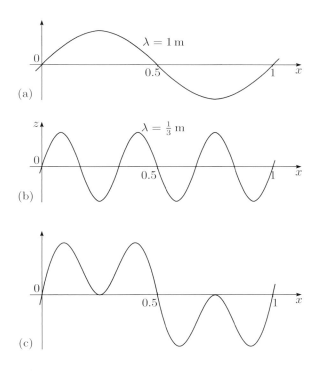

Figure 3.7

(a) If the (combined) wave propagates to the right on water of depth 0.01 m, describe the subsequent shape of the wave after 1 second.

Now suppose that the wave propagates to the right on very deep water.

(b) What is the speed of each individual waveform?

(c) Draw a graph of each waveform showing their positions after 1 second. (Assume that the individual waves retain their shape as they move.)

(d) Hence, from your graphs in part (c), try to sketch the combined wave profile after 1 second.

4 Adding simple waves

For the sake of simplicity, we have so far studied a simple sinusoidal wave of one wavelength; in practice, however, any surface disturbance will usually be a combination of many waves of different wavelengths, frequencies and amplitudes. You have seen that (simple sinusoidal) water waves on deep water are dispersive, i.e. the individual wave speed depends on the wavelength, so that after a certain time the component waves in a disturbance reach different places. For non-dispersive waves (in shallow water), all the component waves in a disturbance travel with the same speed, so that the wave pattern moves along unchanged in shape, with all the individual waves of different wavelengths arriving simultaneously at any given point.

Recall that the water is considered deep (relative to the wavelength) if $h/\lambda \geq 0.5$. The water is shallow if $h/\lambda \leq 0.05$.

Dispersion is discussed on page 32.

One reason for investigating and understanding the properties of simple sinusoidal waves of small amplitude is that a general disturbance like that in Figure 4.1 can be dealt with in terms of sinusoidal waves using Fourier analysis, which involves the superposition of sinusoidal waveforms with many different wavelengths. Without going into the details of this, we can provide an insight into how a linear combination of sinusoidal waves behaves by considering two waves of equal amplitude whose wave numbers and corresponding frequencies are almost equal.

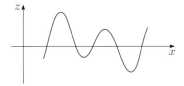

Figure 4.1

We have developed a linear theory of waves, so the Principle of Superposition applies; that is, given several solutions to the equations that model water waves, formulated in Subsection 1.2, any linear combination of these solutions is itself a solution. We have found solutions in terms of sinusoidal functions, so that the sum of two such wave solutions is also a solution to the mathematical problem.

See Equations (1.7) on page 14.

We begin with non-dispersive waves, which, in the context of this unit, are waves on very shallow water, but also include sound waves.

4.1 Non-dispersive waves

The (unscaled) wave number, κ, gives the number of waves per unit length. Here we shall describe the waves in terms of the scaled wave number, $k = 2\pi\kappa$, and the wave speed, c, so that a wave surface profile is described by

$$z = a \cos\left(k(x - ct)\right).$$

Consider two harmonic (sinusoidal) waves with equal amplitude a and almost equal scaled wave numbers, $k - \delta k$ and $k + \delta k$, where $\delta k \ll k$. Since we are considering non-dispersive waves, their wave speeds are equal. Then the combined disturbance is given by

From here on in this section, we shall refer to k as just the wave number.

$$z = a \cos\left((k - \delta k)(x - ct)\right) + a \cos\left((k + \delta k)(x - ct)\right).$$

These two cosines can be added, using the addition formula for cosines, to give

$$z = 2a \cos\left(k(x - ct)\right) \cos\left(\delta k(x - ct)\right). \tag{4.1}$$

Recall that
$$\cos A + \cos B$$
$$= 2\cos\left(\frac{A + B}{2}\right) \cos\left(\frac{B - A}{2}\right).$$

The first cosine factor in this expression represents a wave very similar in shape to the individual waves, but with wave number equal to the average of the two individual wave numbers. The second cosine factor in Equation (4.1) changes much more slowly than the first, both spatially and temporally. For instance, at any fixed time t_0, the wavelength of the 'wave' represented by $\cos(\delta k(x - ct))$ is $2\pi/\delta k$, and since $\delta k \ll k$, this wavelength is much longer than $2\pi/k$, the wavelength of $\cos(k(x - ct))$. Further, at any fixed point x_0, the period between the arrival of wave crests of the 'wave' $\cos(\delta k(x - ct))$ is $2\pi/(c\,\delta k)$, which is much longer than the period for $\cos(k(x - ct))$. The slower spatial change is illustrated in the sketches of the two cosine factors shown in Figure 4.2.

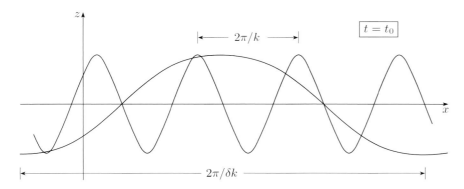

Figure 4.2

We can consider expression (4.1) as the product of a short wave, of wavelength $2\pi/k$, and a long wave, of wavelength $2\pi/\delta k$. Each of these waves moves with the speed of the two original waves.

The following example illustrates the shape of the graph obtained from a function given in the form of Equation (4.1) with $t = 0$.

Example 4.1

Show that the function

$$z = \cos(1.75x) + \cos(2.25x) \qquad\qquad (4.2)$$

can be written as

$$z = 2\cos(2x)\cos(0.25x).$$

Sketch the graph of this function on the interval $-4\pi \le x \le 4\pi$.

Here $a = 1$, $k = 2$, $\delta k = 0.25$ and $t = 0$.

Solution

The addition formula for cosines gives

$$z = 2\cos\left(\frac{1.75 + 2.25}{2}\,x\right)\cos\left(\frac{2.25 - 1.75}{2}\,x\right)$$

$$= 2\cos(2x)\cos(0.25x),$$

as required. The graph of this function is shown in Figure 4.3.   ■

The wavelength of $\cos(2x)$ is π, while the wavelength of $\cos(0.25x)$ is 8π.

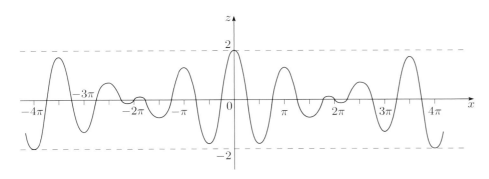

Figure 4.3   Graph of $z = 2\cos(2x)\cos(0.25x)$

Plotting Figure 4.3 accurately is a time-consuming task, unless a computer is used. However, when $\delta k \ll k$ we can more easily sketch the graphs of functions such as that given by Equation (4.2). We now develop this approach, using Figure 4.3 as a guide.

The graph of

$$z = 2\cos(2x)\cos(0.25x)$$

repeats itself after a distance of 8π along the x-axis. Figure 4.3 shows this graph for the interval $-4\pi \le x \le 4\pi$. It is seemingly a very complicated shape, and the properties of the two cosine factors, $\cos(2x)$ and $\cos(0.25x)$, appear to have been lost. The profile height lies in the range $-2 \le z \le 2$, and the distance between consecutive occurrences of the value $z = 2$ (and of $z = -2$) is 8π, which is the wavelength of the factor $\cos(0.25x)$. Figure 4.4 shows (as dashed curves) the graphs of the functions $f_1(x) = 2\cos(0.25x)$ and $f_2(x) = -2\cos(0.25x)$ superimposed on the graph in Figure 4.3.

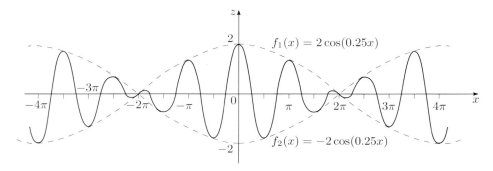

Figure 4.4

The combined wave profile lies between the two dashed curves, touching the graph of each of the functions f_1 and f_2 alternately. These boundary curves are called the *wave envelope*. The wavelength of the wave envelope (which in Example 4.1 is 8π) is much longer than the distance between the peaks (or between the troughs) of the wave profile (see Figure 4.4). This means that the wave will oscillate many times, its amplitude decreasing and increasing continuously between two adjacent zeros of the wave envelope.

The wave profile touches the wave envelope when the factor $\cos(2x)$ attains its maximum and minimum values, that is, when $\cos(2x) = \pm1$; these values occur at $x = -4\pi, -\frac{7}{2}\pi, \ldots, 0, \ldots, \frac{7}{2}\pi, 4\pi$, as shown in Figure 4.4. The maxima and minima of the wave profile are near the points where the wave profile and its envelope touch.

For example, the profile and envelope touch when $x = \pi$, and the profile has a local maximum when $x \simeq 3.08$.

Thus to sketch a wave profile given as the product of two cosine factors,

$$z = 2a\cos(kx)\cos(\delta k\, x),$$

where $\delta k \ll k$, first sketch the wave envelope $z = \pm 2a\cos(\delta k\, x)$ and then, between these curves, sketch the profile, crossing the x-axis at the zeros of $\cos(kx)$ and $\cos(\delta k\, x)$, and touching the envelope at those values of x at which $\cos(kx)$ attains its maxima and minima.

Exercise 4.1

Show that the function

$$z = \cos(2.1x) + \cos(1.9x)$$

can be written as

$$z = 2\cos(2x)\cos(0.1x).$$

Sketch the wave envelope $z = \pm 2\cos(0.1x)$ for the interval $-5\pi \leq x \leq 5\pi$. Hence sketch the wave profile on this interval.

Now we return to the general case of two progressive waves travelling with the same speed but with slightly different wave numbers. The wave profile of the combination is given as before by

$$z = 2a\cos\left(k(x - ct)\right)\cos\left(\delta k(x - ct)\right), \tag{4.1}$$

where $\delta k \ll k$. From the discussion above, we can sketch the wave profile at some given time, t_0 say; the wave envelope has equations

$$z = \pm 2a\cos\left(\delta k(x - ct_0)\right),$$

and the wave profile touches the envelope at the maxima and minima of $\cos\left(k(x - ct_0)\right)$, i.e. at the points $x = ct_0 \pm n\pi/k$. The profile has zeros when $\cos\left(k(x - ct_0)\right) = 0$ and when $\cos\left(\delta k(x - ct_0)\right) = 0$. A typical profile (for which $\delta k/k = 0.05$) is shown in Figure 4.5.

Here, and elsewhere, it is the solid curve which gives the profile of the wave. The dashed curves are constructions to aid in drawing the profile.

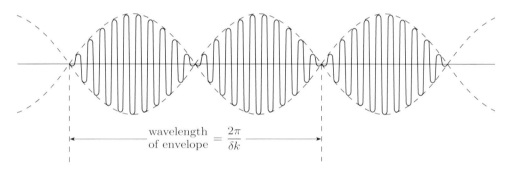

$$\text{wavelength} \atop \text{of envelope} = \frac{2\pi}{\delta k}$$

Figure 4.5

The wave profile in Figure 4.5 shows that the waves appear to come in 'groups' of high and low waves. The high waves are those around the maxima and minima of the envelope, where the component waves reinforce each other, and the low waves are near the zeros of the envelope, where the component waves almost cancel each other out. Since Equation (4.1) can be written as a progressive wave solution, in the form $z = f(x - ct)$, the profile of the combined wave moves to the right with the same speed, c, as the component waves. This is not too surprising; in a non-dispersive motion the wave profile is expected to remain unchanged in time, with all the component waves and any linear combination of them having the same speed.

Since a combined wave profile exhibits many crests and troughs, it is difficult to see how to define 'wavelength' and 'period' for such a wave; the previous definitions given for such terms related only to harmonic waves.

We have spoken of 'groups' of high waves, and you have seen that they are associated with maxima and minima of the wave envelope, which is composed of two harmonic waves. So we now define the *wavelength of a group of waves*, λ_g, to be the (common) wavelength of the envelope curves.

Recall that we are discussing non-dispersive waves here.

For the profile in Equation (4.1), this means that

$$\lambda_g = \frac{2\pi}{\delta k}.$$

With this definition, the distance between successive groups of high waves (or low waves) is $\frac{1}{2}\lambda_g$, as shown in Figure 4.6.

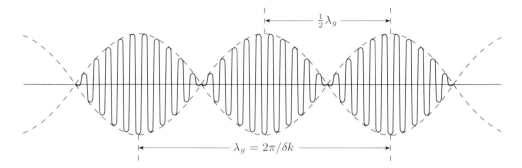

Figure 4.6

Similarly, we can define the *period of a group of waves*, τ_g, as the common period of the envelope curves, so that for the profile of Equation (4.1),

$$\tau_g = \frac{2\pi}{c\,\delta k}.$$

Then successive groups of high crests arrive at a fixed position x_0 at intervals of $\frac{1}{2}\tau_g$.

The *speed* of these groups of waves, c_g, can be interpreted as the speed of the high waves or of the low waves (or as the speed of the zeros in the envelope) and is given by

$$c_g = \frac{\lambda_g}{\tau_g}.$$

This value is the same as c, the speed of the two constituent waves which combine to give the 'group phenomenon'.

Note that it is the wave profile (given by Equation (4.1)) which models physical reality, and that the wave envelope is a feature of the conceptual model.

Note that
$$\frac{\lambda_g}{\tau_g} = \frac{2\pi/\delta k}{2\pi/(c\,\delta k)} = c.$$

Exercise 4.2

Consider two progressive waves,

$$z = \cos\left(1.8(x - 2t)\right) \qquad \text{and} \qquad z = \cos\left(2.2(x - 2t)\right),$$

whose wave numbers differ by a small amount (0.4) but which have the same wave speed $2\,\mathrm{m\,s^{-1}}$. Find the equation of the wave profile formed by the sum of these simple waves, in a form that allows the wave envelope to be identified. Sketch the wave profile for $-5\pi \le x \le 5\pi$ at times $t = 0$ and $t = \frac{1}{2}\pi$. What are the wavelength, period and speed of the group of waves?

The details of the wave profile in the solution to this exercise show that the wave profile does not change shape or position relative to the wave envelope. This is a feature of all non-dispersive waves, because the constituent waves and the group of waves all have the same speed. The analysis of this subsection can be interpreted physically by reference to the phenomenon of *beats* in the theory of sound. Acoustic waves of all frequencies and wavelengths propagate in air with the same speed, so they are non-dispersive waves. If there are two sources of sound with slightly different frequencies, then we hear a resultant signal whose frequency is the average of the two original frequencies but whose intensity fluctuates. The sound appears to be coming in 'pulses', which are often called 'beats'. This phenomenon is particularly noticeable when two guitar strings which are slightly out of tune are plucked simultaneously. It is possible to eliminate the beats by slightly adjusting one of the strings until the fluctuation in the intensity disappears, producing 'clean' notes of the same frequency. Beats can also be detected from a piano that is out of tune, by simultaneously playing a note on it and adding a 'standard' note such as that produced by a tuning fork. Thus, although the wave envelope is part of the conceptual model, the arrival of groups of waves is physically observable.

The intensity (energy flux) of sound is proportional to the square of the amplitude of the sound wave.

4.2   Dispersive waves

Although the analysis for dispersive waves follows the same approach as that for non-dispersive waves in the previous subsection, in this case you will see that the speed of the groups of high and low waves differs quite substantially from the speeds of the component waves.

Consider the combination of two sinusoidal waves, of equal amplitude a but with slightly different wave numbers, $k - \delta k$, $k + \delta k$, and wave speeds, $c - \delta c$, $c + \delta c$, where $\delta k \ll k$ and $\delta c \ll c$. Adding the two component waves, we obtain the combined wave profile

$$z = a \cos\left[(k - \delta k)(x - (c - \delta c)t)\right] + a \cos\left[(k + \delta k)(x - (c + \delta c)t)\right].$$

Applying the cosine addition rule leads to

$$z = 2a \cos\left(k(x - \alpha t)\right) \cos\left(\delta k(x - \beta t)\right), \tag{4.3}$$

where

$$\alpha = \frac{1}{2k}\left[(k - \delta k)(c - \delta c) + (k + \delta k)(c + \delta c)\right]$$

and

$$\beta = \frac{1}{2\,\delta k}\left[(k + \delta k)(c + \delta c) - (k - \delta k)(c - \delta c)\right].$$

Expanding the expressions for α and β and simplifying them gives

$$\alpha = c + \frac{\delta k\,\delta c}{k} \qquad \text{and} \qquad \beta = c + k\frac{\delta c}{\delta k}.$$

Now, since $\delta k \ll k$ and $\delta c \ll c$, we ignore the second-order term $\delta k\,\delta c/k$, so that Equation (4.3) becomes, to first order,

$$z = 2a \cos\left(k(x - ct)\right) \cos\left(\delta k(x - \beta t)\right), \qquad \text{where } \beta = c + k\frac{\delta c}{\delta k}. \tag{4.4}$$

This equation represents the wave profile for the combination of two dispersive waves. Note the similarity to the non-dispersive case discussed in the previous subsection, in that each cosine factor represents a wave; there is a long wave, of wavelength $2\pi/\delta k$, and a short wave, of wavelength $2\pi/k$. However, the speeds associated with these wave factors, c and β, are now different.

The wave profile of the combined wave can be sketched using the same technique as in Subsection 4.1. In the following example, we illustrate the change in shape of the wave profile with time.

Remember that for dispersive waves, $c = c(k)$. For deep water waves,

$$c = \sqrt{\frac{g}{k}}\,;$$

for the finite-depth solution,

$$c = \sqrt{\frac{g}{k}\tanh(kh)}\,.$$

(See pages 21 and 31, respectively, with $2\pi/\lambda = k$.)

Thus $\alpha = c$ to first order.

Example 4.2

Consider the wave profile

$$z = 2\cos\left(2(x - t)\right)\cos\left(0.4(x - \tfrac{1}{2}t)\right),$$

composed of two sinusoidal waves

$$z = \cos\left(1.6(x - 1.1t)\right) \qquad \text{and} \qquad z = \cos\left(2.4(x - 0.9t)\right),$$

with $a = 1$, $c = 1$, $k = 2$, $\delta c = -0.1$ and $\delta k = 0.4$. Sketch the wave profile for $t = 0$ and for $t = \tfrac{1}{2}\pi$.

Solution

For $t = 0$, the wave envelope is given by $z = \pm 2\cos\left(0.4x\right)$. The wave profile is drawn within this envelope so that it crosses the x-axis when $\cos\left(2x\right) = 0$ and touches the envelope at the maxima and minima of $\cos\left(2x\right)$, i.e. when $\cos\left(2x\right) = \pm 1$. The envelope and wave profile are shown in Figure 4.7.

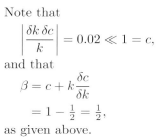

Note that
$$\left|\frac{\delta k\,\delta c}{k}\right| = 0.02 \ll 1 = c,$$
and that
$$\beta = c + k\frac{\delta c}{\delta k}$$
$$= 1 - \tfrac{1}{2} = \tfrac{1}{2},$$
as given above.

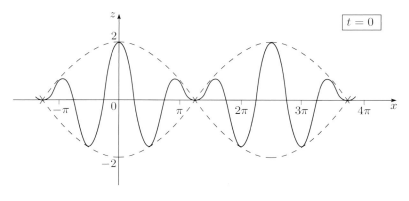

Figure 4.7   The wave profile $z = 2\cos\left(2x\right)\cos\left(0.4x\right)$

For $t = \tfrac{1}{2}\pi$, the wave envelope is given by $z = \pm 2\cos\left(0.4(x - \tfrac{1}{4}\pi)\right)$. The wave profile is drawn within this envelope so that it crosses the x-axis when $\cos\left(2(x - \tfrac{1}{2}\pi)\right) = 0$, i.e. when $\cos\left(2x\right) = 0$. It touches the envelope at the points where $\cos\left(2(x - \tfrac{1}{2}\pi)\right) = \pm 1$, i.e. where $\cos\left(2x\right) = \mp 1$. The envelope and wave profile are shown in Figure 4.8. ■

Recall that
$$\cos(\theta - \pi) = -\cos\theta.$$

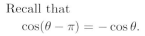

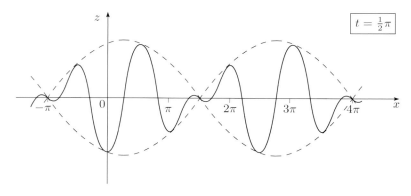

Figure 4.8   The wave profile $z = 2\cos\left(2\left(x - \tfrac{1}{2}\pi\right)\right)\cos\left(0.4\left(x - \tfrac{1}{4}\pi\right)\right)$

Observe from the profiles shown in Figures 4.7 and 4.8 that they change with time relative to the envelope. We can understand this change if we follow the zeros of the envelope cosine factor, $2\cos\left(0.4(x - \tfrac{1}{2}t)\right)$ and the zeros of the factor $\cos\left(2(x - t)\right)$, which together give the zeros of the profile. The former travel with speed $\tfrac{1}{2}$ and the latter move with speed 1.

The wave speed of the progressive wave $z = f(x - ct)$ is c.

A similar observation applies to the wave profile crests. Hence the individual wave crests are travelling forward relative to the envelope.

This changing profile within the envelope contrasts with the non-dispersive case discussed in Subsection 4.1, for which the whole profile travelled along unchanged in shape and with the same speed as the wave envelope. The change in shape for these dispersive waves arises because the component waves, $z_1 = \cos(1.6(x - 1.1t))$ and $z_2 = \cos(2.4(x - 0.9t))$, have different speeds, the longer-wavelength wave (z_1) travelling faster than the shorter-wavelength wave (z_2). This is one of the features of all dispersive water waves, for example.

The composite wave in Example 4.2 shows the change relative to the envelope for a case in which $\delta k/k = 0.2$. If δk is very much less than k, then the wave profile oscillates very rapidly compared to the wave envelope, and its crests and troughs are almost indistinguishable from the wave envelope. For example, Figure 4.9 shows the wave profile of a composite wave for which $\delta k/k = 0.05$.

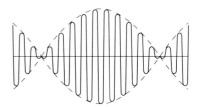

Figure 4.9

In general, dispersive waves appear to come in groups of high and low waves, as for non-dispersive waves. By fixing attention on these groups, we can define a wavelength and period in terms of the wave envelope, as for the non-dispersive case. In the general case, the envelope equations are

$$z = \pm 2a \cos(\delta k(x - \beta t)), \qquad \text{where } \beta = c + k\frac{\delta c}{\delta k}.$$

See Equation (4.4).

Each of these equations is that of a progressive wave. We define the *wavelength of a group of waves*, λ_g, to be the common wavelength of the envelope curves, and the *period of a group of waves*, τ_g, to be the (common) period of the envelope curves, that is,

$$\lambda_g = \frac{2\pi}{\delta k} \qquad \text{and} \qquad \tau_g = \frac{2\pi}{\beta\,\delta k}.$$

The distance between successive groups of high waves is $\frac{1}{2}\lambda_g$, and the difference in times of arrival of successive groups at a particular x-value is $\frac{1}{2}\tau_g$. The *speed* with which these groups travel can be defined by

$$\frac{\lambda_g}{\tau_g}, \qquad \text{which is equal to} \qquad \frac{2\pi/\delta k}{2\pi/(\beta\,\delta k)} = \beta.$$

Now, β is related to the parameters of the two sinusoidal waves whose combination gives the wave profile; we have

$$\beta = c + k\frac{\delta c}{\delta k}.$$

For *non-dispersive* waves, we found that the speed of the group (of high waves) equalled the wave speed of the two sinusoidal waves whose combination was being investigated. For dispersive waves, the situation is different; the speeds of the component sinusoidal waves are not the same, and the speed of the group differs from each of them.

This was because $\delta c = 0$, and hence $\beta = c$.

In Example 4.2, the speeds of the component waves are 1.1 and 0.9, and since the profile equation is

$$z = 2\cos(2(x - t))\cos\left(0.4(x - \tfrac{1}{2}t)\right),$$

the speed of a wave group is $\beta = \frac{1}{2}$, which differs from both 1.1 and 0.9.

For dispersive waves, there is a functional relationship between c and k, so that the two component waves can be expressed in terms of the parameter k; each has the form $z = a\cos(k(x - c(k)t))$.

For example, for water waves in deep water we have $c = \sqrt{g/k}$ (see page 21, with $2\pi/\lambda = k$).

The existence of this functional relationship means that we can express the speed $\beta = c + k\, \delta c/\delta k$ in terms of the derivative dc/dk. If δk is sufficiently small, then δc is small and

$$\frac{\delta c}{\delta k} \simeq \frac{dc}{dk},$$

so that

$$\beta \simeq c + k\frac{dc}{dk}. \tag{4.5}$$

Thus for deep water waves, for example, we have $c = (g/k)^{1/2}$, so that

$$\frac{dc}{dk} = -\tfrac{1}{2}g^{1/2}k^{-3/2} = -\frac{c}{2k},$$

and then $\beta \simeq \tfrac{1}{2}c$.

Since $dc/dk < 0$, we have $\beta < c$ and (below) $c_g < c$.

The quantity on the right-hand side of Equation (4.5) is called the **group velocity**, denoted by c_g, and so we write

$$c_g = c + k\frac{dc}{dk}.$$

This can also be written, using the Product Rule and $c = \omega/k$, as

$$c_g = \frac{d}{dk}(ck) = \frac{d\omega}{dk}.$$

Here c_g is a scalar, so that it would be better to call it the 'group speed'; however, most texts on waves adopt the term 'group velocity'.

The group velocity is the limit as $\delta k \to 0$ of the speed β of the peaks and zeros of the wave envelope of the wave profile produced by adding two sinusoidal waves. Hence the group velocity is the 'envelope velocity'. For non-dispersive waves (see Subsection 4.1), for which c is constant, we have $c_g = c$, so that the group velocity equals the speed of the component waves.

In this case $dc/dk = 0$.

Exercise 4.3

For waves on water of finite depth h, the wave speed c is given in terms of the wave number k by

$$c^2 = \frac{g}{k}\tanh(kh).$$

See page 31, with $2\pi/\lambda = k$.

(a) Show that the group velocity for such waves is

$$c_g = \tfrac{1}{2}c\left(1 + 2kh\,\mathrm{cosech}(2kh)\right).$$

Hints: Start by finding an expression for $d(c^2)/dk$, and then use the given expression for c^2 to obtain c_g as a multiple of c. Several manipulations with hyperbolic functions are required.

(b) Using this formula, show that

(i) if the wavelength is large compared to the depth, so that the shallow water wave theory applies, then the group velocity approximately equals the wave speed;

(ii) if deep water wave theory applies, then the group velocity approximately equals half the wave speed.

Hints: By definition, $\sinh x = \tfrac{1}{2}\left(e^x - e^{-x}\right)$, so that

for small x, $\sinh x \simeq \tfrac{1}{2}\left(1 + x - (1 - x)\right) = x$;

for large x, $\sinh x \simeq \tfrac{1}{2}e^x$.

Recall that

$$\frac{d}{dx}(\tanh x) = \mathrm{sech}^2 x,$$

$$\mathrm{sech}\,x = \frac{1}{\cosh x},$$

$$\mathrm{cosech}\,x = \frac{1}{\sinh x},$$

$$2\sinh x \cosh x = \sinh(2x).$$

Discussion of group velocity

Water waves in general consist of a superposition of waves of various amplitudes and wavelengths. A mathematical treatment of water waves can be developed in terms of a sum of sinusoidal waves of varying amplitudes and wavelengths. You have seen that an analysis of dispersive waves, based on just two sinusoidal waves with wave numbers (and hence wavelengths) differing by a small amount, leads to a complicated wave profile which changes shape continuously. The wave profile appears to the eye to be formed of groups of high and low waves. We have distinguished between the speed of these groups (in the conceptual model this is the speed of the wave envelope) and the speeds of the individual waves forming the sum.

The group velocity (speed of the groups) has been interpreted here geometrically, in terms of what is seen on the water surface. However, it can also be shown that the energy carried by the waves is propagated at the group velocity. How best to extract this energy, to produce power from waves, is a subject of great interest and importance.

While this relatively simple (kinematic) analysis of two waves with slightly differing wave numbers (and hence wavelengths) has predicted the phenomenon of group velocity, a further analysis involving more than two waves with slightly differing wave numbers gives the same formula for the group velocity of propagation. What has been presented here is a simple and brief introduction to a complicated phenomenon. However, the same group velocity ideas can be expected to occur whenever a disturbance consists of a series of simple dispersive waves whose variations in wave properties are small. Observations support this expectation.

Animations of the motion of groups of waves, in both the non-dispersive and dispersive cases, can be seen via Section 2 of the *Media Guide*.

The energy per unit surface area is calculated as $\frac{1}{2}\rho g a^2$, where ρ is the density of water and a is the wave amplitude.

Exercise 4.4

The first sign of an Atlantic storm which may reach the shores of the UK is often provided by the arrival of waves of very long wavelength and of small amplitude, which travel out ahead of the main disturbance. Typically, such waves can be modelled as a sum of sinusoidal waves with individual speeds of about $50\,\mathrm{m\,s^{-1}}$.

(a) If the shallow water wave model applies, estimate how far a group of these waves can travel in a day. What is the corresponding average depth of the ocean, and what is the minimum wavelength for which this model applies?

(b) If the deep water wave model applies, estimate how far a group of these waves can travel in a day. What is the corresponding wavelength (of individual waves), and what is the minimum average depth of ocean for which this model applies?

End-of-section exercise

Exercise 4.5

Consider the composite wave which is the sum of two individual waves

$$z = \cos(0.9x - 0.975t) \qquad \text{and} \qquad z = \cos(1.1x - 1.025t).$$

(a) Sketch the wave envelope and wave profile of the composite wave at times $t = 0$, 2π and 4π, showing the change in the wave profile between two adjacent zeros of the wave envelope.

(b) Describe how the wave profile moves relative to the envelope. What is the value of the group velocity in this case?

(c) How would the behaviour differ if the two individual waves were

$$z = \cos\left(0.9(x - t)\right) \qquad \text{and} \qquad z = \cos\left(1.1(x - t)\right)?$$

5   Waves on a sloping beach

This unit began by describing waves in the oceans and waves caused by a pebble dropped into a pond, and we noted that the nature of these familiar waves is very complicated to model. So we have adopted a simplified approach, and much of the unit has considered harmonic waves propagating through water in a long and wide rectangular channel, so that parallel wave-fronts move directly along the channel. Clearly, such a theory is far from reality. However, in developing it we have managed to extract some of the features that are observed in real water waves. The unit concludes by using this simple theory in a short discussion of a familiar wave phenomenon, namely, that of waves approaching a beach.

To the non-mariner, ocean waves are most apparent during a stroll along the promenade at a coastal resort, or while swimming in the sea. These waves are probably the most fascinating example of all the waves encountered in nature. They begin as a seemingly never-ending stream of well-ordered waves in the distance, but then build up, change direction and profile shape, and crash down on the beach. Some of the features of these waves can be described using the linear theory of this unit, although to explain the actual breaking of the waves requires a non-linear shallow water wave theory.

At some distance from the shore, the waves are nearly uniform progressive waves, with wavelengths that range from a few metres to over 100 m, and corresponding speeds from $4\,\mathrm{m\,s^{-1}}$ to about $20\,\mathrm{m\,s^{-1}}$. These waves can be modelled as sinusoidal waves, approaching the shore in parallel wave-fronts. Of course, when out in the deep ocean, the wave-fronts are not necessarily parallel to the line of the beach, as indicated in Figure 5.1. As the waves approach the beach, the depth of water is reduced and two features are apparent. Firstly, the line of wave crests becomes more closely parallel to that of the beach, and consequently the wave appears to 'bend round'; we say that the waves are *refracted*. A second feature, perhaps less noticeable than the first, is that the distance between successive crests is

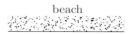

beach

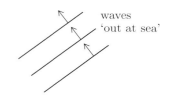

waves 'out at sea'

Figure 5.1

reduced and the amplitude increases. This phase of the motion can be described by the linear theory, as will be explained shortly.

In the final stages, the wave amplitude begins to grow more rapidly, the peaks tend to steepen, and the wave no longer takes the form of a sinusoidal wave. Eventually, if the beach is steep enough, the water curls over the crest and the wave breaks. The photograph in Figure 5.2 illustrates a breaking wave.

Figure 5.2   A wave breaking

This final phase, the build-up and breaking of the waves, requires a non-linear theory. During the process of the wave breaking, the energy that the wave possesses is dissipated. For moderate waves, of initial wavelength 10 m, the wave speed falls from around $4\,\mathrm{m\,s^{-1}}$ to less than $1\,\mathrm{m\,s^{-1}}$ when the depth is 0.1 m. As the speed reduces, the amplitude of the wave increases because kinetic energy is converted to potential energy. The effect of the beach is to slow down the lower water so that the top of the wave is travelling quicker than the bottom. In the actual breaking, the energy is converted partially into heat, through turbulence, and partially into the energy of a secondary flow. When a wave breaks, the water is projected up the beach, where gravity will tend to return it to the main body of water. However, before it can trickle back, the next wave crashes down, sending further water up the beach and holding the water from the earlier wave. After several minutes and successive waves, the amount of water projected up the beach becomes so large that it rushes back down the beach in a torrent. This current may be strong enough to topple bathers off their feet and sweep them seawards.

This is a viscous effect near a boundary.

This secondary flow is sometimes called a 'rip current' or 'undertow'.

The refraction and wavelength changes are easily described with the linear theory. Consider a simple situation in which a train of waves of one particular wavelength, λ_0 say, is approaching a sloping beach (see Figure 5.1). Some distance from the beach, the waves can be modelled using the deep water wave theory. However, as the depth of water decreases, the speed of the wave decreases (see Figure 5.3), although the frequency remains constant. The effect of this speed change is to slow down that part of a wave-front in shallow water relative to another part of the wave-front in deeper water. In Figure 5.4, the part of the wave at Y is travelling more slowly than that at X, so that the wave appears to bend round and become gradually nearer to being in line with the beach; in other words, as the wave approaches the beach, X catches up with Y.

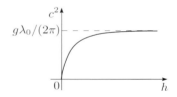

Figure 5.3

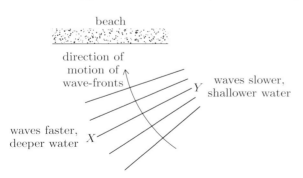

Figure 5.4

Similarly, the wavelength decreases (the waves become more 'bunched up') because the speed closer to the beach (in shallower water) is reduced relative to the speed further from the beach (in deeper water). The frequency remains constant because the period $\tau = \lambda/c$ between successive wave-fronts remains the same throughout the motion. If this were not so (in a quasi-steady-state situation), the wave-fronts would take different times to reach the beach from a given starting point.

47

Refraction in sea waves explains the curved wave-fronts in the photograph of waves in Scarborough Bay shown in Figure 5.5. The beach here is curved, and the wave-fronts, which out at sea are initially straight, curve round with their 'centres' leaving the 'edges' behind. This is another example of dispersion, in which both wave speed and wavelength reduce with diminishing depth of water.

Figure 5.5   Refraction of waves in Scarborough Bay

In fact, the refraction of water waves is more complicated than the explanation given here suggests, because the change in speed causes the waves to change wavelength, in addition to the change caused just by reduction of depth. Furthermore, at the outset there are waves of many wavelengths approaching the beach, so that a fuller theory would need to be in terms of the groups of waves. However, the linear theory and the simple sinusoidal wave solution provide a good start at modelling waves on the deep ocean and in the intermediate zone before the wave-breaking region.

Outcomes

After studying this unit you should be able to:

- explain the derivation of the linearised water wave model, to obtain equations for the velocity potential function;
- apply the relationship between the velocity potential function and the surface profile function;
- within the linearised model, find the form of solution for the velocity potential function that involves a sinusoidal progressive wave;
- derive the velocity potential function, wave condition, wave speed and surface profile function for the case of waves in deep water;
- show that the particle paths for waves in deep water are circular;
- derive the velocity potential function, wave condition, wave speed and surface profile function for the case of waves in water of finite depth;
- show that the particle paths for waves in water of finite depth are elliptical;
- given a wavelength and depth of water, test whether the wave motion is covered by the theory for shallow water, deep water or neither, and apply the appropriate expression for wave speed in each case;
- explain the difference between dispersive and non-dispersive waves;
- explain the effect of combining two sinusoidal waves with equal amplitude but different wave numbers, in the non-dispersive case;
- explain the effect of combining two sinusoidal waves with equal amplitude but different wave numbers and speeds, in the dispersive case;
- describe the motion of a combination of two sinusoidal waves in terms of the motion of the wave envelope and the motion within the wave envelope;
- calculate the group velocity for waves in either deep water or water of finite depth, and explain what this represents;
- apply the linearised water wave model to explain the refraction of waves approaching a sloping beach.

Acknowledgements

Grateful acknowledgement is made to the following sources:

Figures 1.4 and 5.2: © PhotoDisc Europe;

Figures 1.6 and 2.2: *NCFMF Book of Film Notes*, 1974, The MIT Press with Education Development Center Inc, Newton MA;

Figure 3.6: From *La Houille Blanche*, 1950, vol. 5 © Société Hydrotechnique de France;

Figure 5.5: Mr B.C.P. Goss.

Every effort has been made to contact copyright holders. If any have been inadvertently overlooked the publishers will be pleased to make the necessary arrangements at the first opportunity.

Solutions to the exercises

Section 1

Solution 1.1

Bernoulli's equation, with the u^2 term neglected, can be applied in each liquid. In the upper liquid, of density ρ_1, the pressure p_1 is given by

$$\frac{\partial \phi_1}{\partial t} + gz = \frac{p_0 - p_1}{\rho_1} \quad \text{(to first order)},$$

where p_0 is the pressure at the equilibrium interface (taken as $z = 0$). In the lower liquid, of density ρ_2, the pressure p_2 is given by

$$\frac{\partial \phi_2}{\partial t} + gz = \frac{p_0 - p_2}{\rho_2} \quad \text{(to first order)}.$$

Now, at the interface $z = \zeta$ and $p_1 = p_2$ (and hence $p_0 - p_1 = p_0 - p_2$); thus we can write an 'interface condition' as

$$\rho_1 \left(\frac{\partial \phi_1}{\partial t} \right)_{z=\zeta} + \rho_1 g\, \zeta = \rho_2 \left(\frac{\partial \phi_2}{\partial t} \right)_{z=\zeta} + \rho_2 g\, \zeta.$$

Using the Taylor expansions for $(\partial \phi_1/\partial t)_{z=\zeta}$ and $(\partial \phi_2/\partial t)_{z=\zeta}$ about $z = 0$ gives, to first order,

$$\rho_1 \left(\frac{\partial \phi_1}{\partial t} \right)_{z=0} + \rho_1 g\, \zeta = \rho_2 \left(\frac{\partial \phi_2}{\partial t} \right)_{z=0} + \rho_2 g\, \zeta.$$

Solution 1.2

Equation (1.8) is

$$\zeta = -\frac{1}{g} \left(\frac{\partial \phi}{\partial t} \right)_{z=0}.$$

If $\phi = D \cosh\left(k(z+h)\right) \cos(kx - \omega t)$, then

$$\frac{\partial \phi}{\partial t} = D\omega \cosh\left(k(z+h)\right) \sin(kx - \omega t).$$

Hence, putting $z = 0$, we have

$$\zeta = -\frac{D\omega \cosh(kh)}{g} \sin(kx - \omega t).$$

The amplitude of the surface profile is

$$\frac{|D\omega| \cosh(kh)}{g}.$$

(Recall that the amplitude is positive.)

Solution 1.3

(a) False; the surface profile is given by the graph of ζ.

(b) False; while ϕ satisfies Laplace's equation, for every value of t, the function $\zeta(x,t)$ satisfies the wave equation (and not Laplace's equation).

(c) False; pressure changes can be detected throughout the fluid.

(d) True; see Assumption 6.

Solution 1.4

Equation (1.9) is

$$\left(\frac{\partial \phi}{\partial t} \right)_{z=0} = -ag \sin(kx - \omega t).$$

Using $\phi(x, z, t) = Z(z) \cos(kx - \omega t)$, we obtain

$$\left(\frac{\partial \phi}{\partial t} \right)_{z=0} = Z(0)\, \omega \sin(kx - \omega t).$$

Hence Equation (1.9) is satisfied provided that $Z(0) = -ag/\omega$.

Solution 1.5

Laplace's equation for ϕ is $\partial^2\phi/\partial x^2 + \partial^2\phi/\partial z^2 = 0$. Now with $\phi(x, z, t) = Z(z) \cos(kx - \omega t)$, we have

$$\frac{\partial^2 \phi}{\partial x^2} = -k^2 Z(z) \cos(kx - \omega t),$$

$$\frac{\partial^2 \phi}{\partial z^2} = Z''(z) \cos(kx - \omega t).$$

Hence

$$\left[-k^2 Z(z) + Z''(z) \right] \cos(kx - \omega t) = 0.$$

For this equation to hold for all x and t, the function $Z(z)$ must be a solution of

$$Z'' - k^2 Z = 0.$$

The general solution of this is

$$Z(z) = Ae^{-kz} + Be^{kz},$$

where A and B are arbitrary constants, or equivalently,

$$Z(z) = D \cosh\left(k(z+h)\right) + E \sinh\left(k(z+h)\right),$$

where D and E are arbitrary constants.

Solution 1.6

We are given that the period (τ) is $2\,\text{s}$, the wavelength (λ) is $4\,\text{m}$ and the amplitude (a) is $0.1\,\text{m}$. The surface profile is given by

$$z = \zeta(x,t) = a \sin(kx - \omega t),$$

where $k = 2\pi/\lambda = \frac{1}{2}\pi$ and $\omega = 2\pi/\tau = \pi$. So

$$\zeta(x,t) \simeq 0.1 \sin\left(\pi(\tfrac{1}{2}x - t)\right).$$

The velocity potential function is

$$\phi(x, z, t) = Z(z) \cos\left(\pi(\tfrac{1}{2}x - t)\right),$$

where $Z(z) = Ae^{-kz} + Be^{kz}$ and $k = \frac{1}{2}\pi$. Then to satisfy the condition $\lim_{z \to -\infty} \phi = 0$, we must choose $A = 0$. At the surface,

$$\left(\frac{\partial \phi}{\partial t} \right)_{z=0} = -g\zeta = -0.1g \sin\left(\pi(\tfrac{1}{2}x - t)\right).$$

From above, we also have

$$\left(\frac{\partial \phi}{\partial t} \right)_{z=0} = -B(-\pi) \sin\left(\pi(\tfrac{1}{2}x - t)\right).$$

Thus $B = -0.1g/\pi$, and so

$$\phi(x, z, t) = -\frac{0.1g}{\pi} e^{\pi z/2} \cos\left(\pi(\tfrac{1}{2}x - t)\right)$$

$$\simeq -0.31 e^{\pi z/2} \cos\left(\pi(\tfrac{1}{2}x - t)\right).$$

Solution 1.7

Here $k = \pi$ and $\omega = 6\pi$. Hence we have

wave number: $\quad \kappa = k/(2\pi) = \frac{1}{2}$,

wavelength: $\quad \lambda = 2\pi/k = 2\,\mathrm{m}$,

wave speed: $\quad c = \omega/k = 6\,\mathrm{m\,s^{-1}}$,

period: $\quad \tau = 2\pi/\omega = \frac{1}{3}\,\mathrm{s}$.

The surface profile function is obtained from Equation (1.8),

$$\zeta = -\frac{1}{g}\left(\frac{\partial \phi}{\partial t}\right)_{z=0}.$$

With $\phi(x, z, t) = 0.05 \cosh\left(\pi(z + 0.1)\right) \cos\left(\pi(x - 6t)\right)$, we have

$$\left(\frac{\partial \phi}{\partial t}\right)_{z=0} = 0.05 \cosh(0.1\pi) \times 6\pi \sin\left(\pi(x - 6t)\right).$$

Thus

$$\zeta(x, t) = -\frac{0.3\pi}{g} \cosh(0.1\pi) \sin\left(\pi(x - 6t)\right)$$

$$\simeq -0.10 \sin\left(\pi(x - 6t)\right).$$

The amplitude of the surface wave profile is $0.10\,\mathrm{m}$.

Section 2

Solution 2.1

At the free surface, Equation (1.7b) holds, that is,

$$\frac{\partial^2 \phi}{\partial t^2} + g\frac{\partial \phi}{\partial z} = 0 \quad \text{at } z = 0.$$

On the channel floor, the normal boundary condition gives

$$(u_3 =) \ \frac{\partial \phi}{\partial z} = 0 \quad \text{when } z = -\infty,$$

or

$$\lim_{z \to -\infty} \frac{\partial \phi}{\partial z} = 0.$$

(This is also obtained from Equation (1.7c) in the limit as $h \to \infty$.)

Solution 2.2

Following the steps in Example 2.1, we have (to 3 significant figures)

$$\omega = \frac{2\pi}{\tau} = \frac{2\pi}{\frac{1}{4}} = 8\pi \simeq 25.1\,\mathrm{s^{-1}},$$

$$k = \frac{\omega^2}{g} = \frac{64\pi^2}{g} \simeq 64.4\,\mathrm{m^{-1}}.$$

Hence

$$\phi(x, z, t) = Be^{64.4z} \cos(64.4x - 25.1t).$$

The wave speed, c, is given by

$$c = \frac{\omega}{k} = \frac{g}{8\pi} = 0.390\,\mathrm{m\,s^{-1}} \quad \text{(to 3 s.f.)}.$$

The wavelength, λ, is given by

$$\lambda = \frac{2\pi}{k} = \frac{g}{32\pi} = 0.0976\,\mathrm{m} \quad \text{(to 3 s.f.)}.$$

No value can be deduced for the amplitude in this case, since B is unspecified. (Notice, however, that the amplitude varies exponentially with depth.)

Solution 2.3

We are given $\lambda = 10\,\mathrm{m}$, so that $k = 2\pi/\lambda \simeq 0.628\,\mathrm{m^{-1}}$ and then $\omega = \sqrt{gk} \simeq 2.48\,\mathrm{s^{-1}}$. Hence

$$\phi(x, z, t) = Be^{0.628z} \cos(0.628x - 2.48t).$$

The period τ and wave speed c are given by

$$\tau = \frac{2\pi}{\omega} \simeq 2.53\,\mathrm{s} \quad \text{and} \quad c = \frac{\omega}{k} \simeq 3.95\,\mathrm{m\,s^{-1}}.$$

(All calculations are correct to 3 significant figures.)

Solution 2.4

For an 'infinite-depth' gravity wave, we have the velocity potential function

$$\phi(x, z, t) = Be^{kz} \cos(kx - \omega t).$$

The surface profile is $z = \zeta(x, t)$, where, from Equation (1.8),

$$\zeta = -\frac{1}{g}\left(\frac{\partial \phi}{\partial t}\right)_{z=0},$$

so that

$$\zeta(x, t) = -\frac{B\omega}{g} \sin(kx - \omega t).$$

(For the surface profile, the wavelength λ, speed c and period τ are given by

$$\lambda = \frac{2\pi}{k}, \qquad c = \frac{\omega}{k} \quad \text{and} \quad \tau = \frac{2\pi}{\omega}.$$

These give the same values as for the velocity potential function.)

If a is the amplitude of the surface profile (i.e. 'what we see'), then

$$a = \frac{B\omega}{g},$$

where B is the surface amplitude of ϕ. Using $\omega^2 = gk$ (Equation (2.4)), this can also be written as $a = Bk/\omega = B/c$.

Solution 2.5

In the infinitely deep water model, $\omega^2 = gk$, so that the period τ is

$$\tau = \frac{2\pi}{\omega} = \frac{2\pi}{\sqrt{gk}} = \sqrt{\frac{2\pi\lambda}{g}};$$

hence,

$$\lambda = \frac{g\tau^2}{2\pi}.$$

Putting $\tau = 120\,\mathrm{s}$ gives $\lambda \simeq 22\,000\,\mathrm{m}$. No ship is $11\,000\,\mathrm{m}$ long; so the seaman's tale cannot be believed.

Solution 2.6

If the waves have wavelength $10\,\mathrm{m}$, then the speed of the waves is $c = \sqrt{\lambda g/(2\pi)} \simeq 4\,\mathrm{m\,s^{-1}}$. In 4 seconds, a wave crest travels 16 metres. In that time, an observer on the boat sees the crest travel from the stern to the bow of the boat, a length of $10\,\mathrm{m}$ relative to the boat, so that in 4 seconds the boat has travelled 6 metres. Hence the speed of the boat is about $1.5\,\mathrm{m\,s^{-1}}$.

Solution 2.7

(a) The radius of the circular pathline at a depth z_0 is

$$r_0 = a\,e^{kz_0}.$$

For a particle with centre at a depth of half a wavelength, having $z_0 = -\frac{1}{2}\lambda = -\pi/k$, the radius is

$$r_1 = a\,e^{-\pi}.$$

For a particle with centre at depth $z_0 = 0$, the radius is

$$r_2 = a.$$

The ratio r_1/r_2 is then $e^{-\pi} = 0.043$ (to 2 significant figures), and so r_1 is less than 5% of r_2.

(b) The wave condition (2.4) is $\omega^2 = gk$. For a higher frequency $f = \omega/(2\pi)$, the scaled wave number $k = \omega^2/g$ will be larger. Since $z_0 < 0$, the corresponding value of the radius $r = a\,e^{kz_0}$ of particle paths will be smaller.

(Hence with higher-frequency surface waves there is less disturbance beneath the surface.)

Solution 2.8

Suppose that the distance from the storm to the weather station is D (in metres). Then, if the two waves travel with speeds c_1 (for $\lambda_1 = 8\,\text{m}$) and c_2 (for $\lambda_2 = 1\frac{1}{2}\,\text{m}$), the times taken for each wave to arrive at the weather station are D/c_1 and D/c_2, respectively. Using the 'deep water' wave formula relating c to λ (see page 21), we have

$$c_1 = \sqrt{\frac{g\lambda_1}{2\pi}} \simeq 3.53\,\text{m s}^{-1}$$

and

$$c_2 = \sqrt{\frac{g\lambda_2}{2\pi}} \simeq 1.53\,\text{m s}^{-1}.$$

According to the observations, the shorter waves take 12 hours longer to arrive than the long waves. Hence

$$\frac{D}{c_2} - \frac{D}{c_1} = 12 \times 60 \times 60,$$

and so

$$D = \frac{12 \times 60 \times 60}{1/c_2 - 1/c_1} \simeq 1.17 \times 10^5\,\text{m}.$$

Hence the storm is approximately 117 km from the weather station.

The time taken for the long waves to arrive is

$$\frac{D}{c_1} \simeq \frac{1.17 \times 10^5}{3.53} \simeq 33.0 \times 10^3\,\text{s},$$

or approximately 9 hours. Hence the waves started from the area of the storm at about 21:00 on the Sunday evening.

Solution 2.9

We use the formula $\omega = 2\pi/\tau$ to find ω. Then, since the wave condition $\omega^2 = gk$ holds, we have

$$\lambda = \frac{2\pi}{k} = \frac{2\pi g}{\omega^2} \qquad \text{and} \qquad c = \frac{\omega}{k} = \frac{g}{\omega}.$$

With $\tau = 2.5$, we have $\omega = 0.8\pi \simeq 2.51$, and then

$$\lambda = \frac{2\pi g}{0.64\pi^2} \simeq 9.76 \qquad \text{and} \qquad c = \frac{g}{0.8\pi} \simeq 3.90.$$

The wave has wavelength 9.76 m and speed $3.90\,\text{m s}^{-1}$.

Hence, $\phi(x, z, t) = B e^{kz} \cos(kx - \omega t)$, where $k = 2\pi/\lambda \simeq 0.644$ and $\omega \simeq 2.51$; that is,

$$\phi(x, z, t) \simeq B e^{0.644z} \cos(0.644x - 2.51t).$$

The value of B can be found from the amplitude a of the surface profile, given as $\frac{1}{2}$ m in the question. From Solution 2.4, $B = ga/\omega$. Hence

$$B \simeq \frac{g}{2 \times 2.51} \simeq 1.95.$$

The velocity potential function is therefore

$$\phi(x, z, t) \simeq 1.95 e^{0.644z} \cos(0.644x - 2.51t).$$

For the deep water wave theory to apply, we require the depth h to satisfy $h \geq \frac{1}{2}\lambda$. Since for this wave $\lambda = 9.76\,\text{m}$, we require the depth to be greater than 4.88 m.

The pathlines are circles of radii

$$r = a e^{kz_0} = \frac{1}{2} e^{kz_0}.$$

The following table gives these radii at the required depths. (If $z_0 = -p\lambda$, then $\frac{1}{2} e^{kz_0} = \frac{1}{2} e^{-2\pi p}$.)

z_0/λ	0	-0.1	-0.5	-2
r	0.5	0.267	0.0216	1.74×10^{-6}

Section 3

Solution 3.1

(a) By definition,

$$\tanh x = \frac{e^x - e^{-x}}{e^x + e^{-x}} = \frac{1 - e^{-2x}}{1 + e^{-2x}}.$$

Hence

$$\tanh(kx) = \frac{1 - e^{-2kx}}{1 + e^{-2kx}}.$$

Since $e^{-2kx} \to 0$ as $x \to \infty$, we have

$$\lim_{x \to \infty} \tanh(kx) = \lim_{x \to \infty} \left(\frac{1 - e^{-2kx}}{1 + e^{-2kx}} \right) = \frac{1}{1} = 1.$$

(b) The Taylor series for $f(x)$ about $x = 0$ is

$$f(0) + f'(0)x + \tfrac{1}{2}f''(0)x^2 + \cdots + \frac{1}{n!}f^{(n)}(0)x^n + \cdots.$$

With $f(x) = \tanh x$, we have

$$f(0) = 0,$$
$$f'(0) = \text{sech}^2 0 = 1,$$
$$f''(0) = -2\,\text{sech}^2 0 \tanh 0 = 0,$$
$$f'''(0) = -2(-2\,\text{sech}^2 0 \tanh^2 0 + \text{sech}^4 0) = -2.$$

Hence

$$\tanh x = x - \tfrac{1}{3}x^3 + \cdots,$$
$$\frac{\tanh x}{x} = 1 - \tfrac{1}{3}x^2 + \cdots,$$

and so

$$\lim_{x \to 0} \left(\frac{\tanh x}{x} \right) = 1.$$

Solution 3.2

According to Frame 9, the deep water wave model applies when $h \geq 0.5\lambda$, and the shallow water wave model applies when $h \leq 0.05\lambda$. The following table shows the model to be used and the wave speed for each case.

For the deep water wave model, we use $c^2 = \lambda g/(2\pi)$, and for the shallow water wave model, we use $c^2 = gh$; otherwise, we use

$$c^2 = \frac{\lambda g}{2\pi} \tanh\left(\frac{2\pi h}{\lambda}\right),$$

which in fact works in all cases.

h (m)	h/λ	model	wave speed ($\mathrm{m\,s^{-1}}$)
0.1	0.025	shallow	0.99
0.3	0.075	exact	1.66
1.9	0.475	exact	2.49
10	2.5	deep	2.50

Solution 3.3

Since $h/\lambda = 5/50 = 0.1 < 0.5$, the deep water wave model is not appropriate here. Furthermore $h/\lambda > 0.05$, so that the 'exact' solution must be used.

From Frame 9, we have

$$c^2 = \frac{\lambda g}{2\pi} \tanh\left(\frac{2\pi h}{\lambda}\right) \simeq 43\,474,$$

so that $c \simeq 208.5\,\mathrm{m\,s^{-1}}$; also

$$\omega = \frac{2\pi c}{\lambda} \simeq 0.0262\,\mathrm{s^{-1}} \quad \text{and} \quad \tau = \frac{2\pi}{\omega} \simeq 239.8\,\mathrm{s}.$$

The velocity potential function is

$$\phi(x, z, t) = D \cosh\left(k(z + h)\right) \cos(kx - \omega t),$$

where $k = 2\pi/\lambda \simeq 1.26 \times 10^{-4}\,\mathrm{m^{-1}}$. Hence,

$\phi \simeq D \cosh\left(0.00013(z + 5000)\right) \cos(0.00013x - 0.026t)$.

From Frame 5A, the surface profile has equation

$$z = \zeta(x, t) = -\frac{1}{g}\left(\frac{\partial \phi}{\partial t}\right)_{z=0}$$

$$= -\frac{D\omega}{g} \cosh(kh) \sin(kx - \omega t)$$

$$\simeq -3.22 \times 10^{-3} D \sin(0.00013x - 0.026t).$$

Nothing can be said about the wave amplitude from the information given.

Solution 3.4

If $h = 0.01$, we have:

for $\lambda = 1$, $\quad h/\lambda = 0.01 < 0.05$;

for $\lambda = \frac{1}{2}$, $\quad h/\lambda = 0.02 < 0.05$.

Thus we can use the shallow water wave model, for which each simple wave travels with the same speed. Hence, the combined wave in Figure 3.3(c) will travel, keeping the same shape, at speed $\sqrt{gh} \simeq 0.31\,\mathrm{m\,s^{-1}}$. The waves are non-dispersive.

Solution 3.5

(a) The pathline equations in Cartesian coordinates are

$$\frac{dx}{dt} = u_1 = \frac{\partial \phi}{\partial x} = -kD \cosh\left(k(z + h)\right) \sin(kx - \omega t),$$

$$\frac{dz}{dt} = u_3 = \frac{\partial \phi}{\partial z} = kD \sinh\left(k(z + h)\right) \cos(kx - \omega t).$$

(b) In terms of $X = x - x_0$ and $Z = z - z_0$, we have

$$\frac{dX}{dt} = -kD \cosh\left(k(z_0 + Z + h)\right) \sin(k(x_0 + X) - \omega t),$$

$$\frac{dZ}{dt} = kD \sinh\left(k(z_0 + Z + h)\right) \cos(k(x_0 + X) - \omega t).$$

Expanding the right-hand sides as Taylor series about $(X, Z) = (0, 0)$, we have

$$\begin{aligned}\frac{dX}{dt} = &- kD \cosh\left(k(z_0 + h)\right) \sin(kx_0 - \omega t) \\ &- k^2 D \cosh\left(k(z_0 + h)\right) \cos(kx_0 - \omega t)\,X \\ &- k^2 D \sinh\left(k(z_0 + h)\right) \sin(kx_0 - \omega t)\,Z \\ &+ kD \times O(k^2 X^2, k^2 XZ, k^2 Z^2),\end{aligned}$$

$$\begin{aligned}\frac{dZ}{dt} = &\, kD \sinh\left(k(z_0 + h)\right) \cos(kx_0 - \omega t) \\ &- k^2 D \sinh\left(k(z_0 + h)\right) \sin(kx_0 - \omega t)\,X \\ &+ k^2 D \cosh\left(k(z_0 + h)\right) \cos(kx_0 - \omega t)\,Z \\ &+ kD \times O(k^2 X^2, k^2 XZ, k^2 Z^2).\end{aligned}$$

Retaining only the first term of each, since kX, kZ and kD are small enough to ignore products of these, we obtain

$$\frac{dX}{dt} = -kD \cosh\left(k(z_0 + h)\right) \sin(kx_0 - \omega t),$$

$$\frac{dZ}{dt} = kD \sinh\left(k(z_0 + h)\right) \cos(kx_0 - \omega t).$$

(c) Integrating these two equations gives

$$X = -\frac{kD}{\omega} \cosh\left(k(z_0 + h)\right) \cos(kx_0 - \omega t),$$

$$Z = -\frac{kD}{\omega} \sinh\left(k(z_0 + h)\right) \sin(kx_0 - \omega t).$$

Eliminating t, we have

$$\left(\frac{\omega X}{kD \cosh\left(k(z_0 + h)\right)}\right)^2 + \left(\frac{\omega Z}{kD \sinh\left(k(z_0 + h)\right)}\right)^2 = 1.$$

This is the equation of an ellipse with semi-major axis $(kD/\omega) \cosh\left(k(z_0 + h)\right)$ and semi-minor axis $(kD/\omega) \sinh\left(k(z_0 + h)\right)$.

Solution 3.6

(a) For each component wave, $h/\lambda \leq 0.05$, so that the shallow water wave theory applies and each wave travels with the same speed. Hence the superposed wave profile does not change shape. (In 1 second it moves a distance $\sqrt{gh} \simeq 0.31\,\mathrm{m}$ to the right.)

(b) Using the deep water wave analysis, we have $c = \sqrt{g\lambda/(2\pi)}$. Thus $\lambda = 1$ gives $c \simeq 1.25\,\mathrm{m\,s^{-1}}$, and $\lambda = \frac{1}{3}$ gives $c \simeq 0.72\,\mathrm{m\,s^{-1}}$.

(c) After 1 second, the longer-wavelength wave has travelled 1.25 m, and the shorter-wavelength wave has travelled 0.72 m. Their relative positions are shown in the following figures.

53

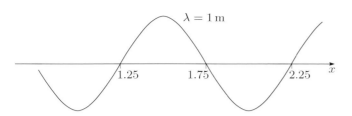

$\lambda = 1\,\text{m}$

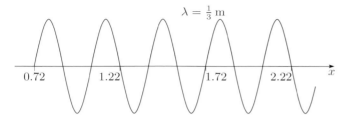

$\lambda = \frac{1}{3}\,\text{m}$

(d) After adding the displacements, the combined wave profile can be sketched as shown below. This differs from the shape of the graph in Figure 3.7(c).

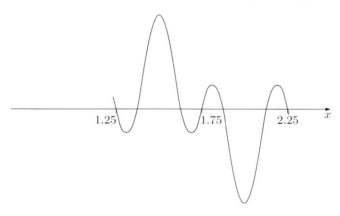

Section 4

Solution 4.1

Using the addition formula for cosines, we have
$$z = 2\cos\left(\frac{1.9 + 2.1}{2}x\right)\cos\left(\frac{2.1 - 1.9}{2}x\right)$$
$$= 2\cos(2x)\cos(0.1x).$$

The figure below shows a sketch of this composite wave profile. The dashed curves represent the wave envelope, $z = \pm 2\cos(0.1x)$. The zeros of the wave profile are given by $\cos(2x) = 0$ and by $\cos(0.1x) = 0$; that is, there are zeros at $x = \pm\frac{1}{4}(2n+1)\pi$ for $n = 0, 1, \ldots, 9$, and at $x = \pm 5\pi$. In the interval $-5\pi \le x \le 5\pi$, the wave profile touches the wave envelope at the points for which $\cos(2x) = \pm 1$, namely, $\pm\frac{1}{2}n\pi$ for $n = 0, 1, \ldots, 9$.

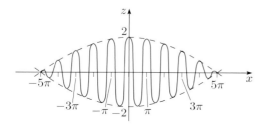

Solution 4.2

The composite wave has equation
$$z = \cos(1.8(x - 2t)) + \cos(2.2(x - 2t))$$
$$= 2\cos(2(x - 2t))\cos(0.2(x - 2t)).$$
The wave envelope has equations
$$z = \pm 2\cos(0.2(x - 2t)).$$
At $t = 0$, we have
$$z = 2\cos(2x)\cos(0.2x),$$
and at $t = \frac{1}{2}\pi$, we have
$$z = 2\cos(2(x - \pi))\cos(0.2(x - \pi))$$
$$= 2\cos(2x)\cos(0.2(x - \pi)).$$
The following figures show sketches of each of these profiles for $-5\pi \le x \le 5\pi$.

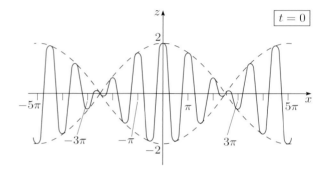

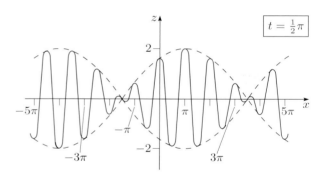

The wavelength and period of the group of waves are respectively $2\pi/0.2$ and $2\pi/(2 \times 0.2)$, that is,
$$\lambda_g = 10\pi\,\text{m} \qquad\text{and}\qquad \tau_g = 5\pi\,\text{s}.$$
Hence, $c_g = \lambda_g/\tau_g = 2\,\text{m s}^{-1}$.

(Alternatively, $c_g = c = 2\,\text{m s}^{-1}$. The second graph above is obtained easily by noting that, after time $\frac{1}{2}\pi$, the first profile will have moved a distance $2 \times \frac{1}{2}\pi = \pi$ to the right.)

Solution 4.3

(a) For waves on the surface of water of depth h, we have
$$c^2 = \frac{g}{k}\tanh(kh).$$
Hence, differentiating with respect to k, we obtain
$$2c\frac{dc}{dk} = -\frac{g}{k^2}\tanh(kh) + \frac{hg}{k}\text{sech}^2(kh).$$
The group velocity c_g is defined by
$$c_g = c + k\frac{dc}{dk}.$$

In this case,
$$c_g = c + \frac{k}{2c}\left(-\frac{g}{k^2}\tanh(kh) + \frac{hg}{k}\operatorname{sech}^2(kh)\right)$$
$$= c + \frac{kg}{2ck^2}\tanh(kh)\left(-1 + hk\operatorname{sech}(kh)\operatorname{cosech}(kh)\right)$$
$$= c + \tfrac{1}{2}c\left(-1 + hk\operatorname{sech}(kh)\operatorname{cosech}(kh)\right)$$
$$= \tfrac{1}{2}c\left(1 + hk\operatorname{sech}(kh)\operatorname{cosech}(kh)\right).$$

Now
$$\operatorname{sech}(kh)\operatorname{cosech}(kh) = \frac{1}{\sinh(kh)\cosh(kh)}$$
$$= \frac{1}{\frac{1}{2}\sinh(2kh)},$$
so that
$$c_g = \tfrac{1}{2}c\left(1 + 2kh\operatorname{cosech}(2kh)\right).$$

(b) (i) For shallow water wave theory, $\lambda \gg h$, so that $kh \ll 1$ (since $k = 2\pi/\lambda$). With this approximation,
$$\operatorname{cosech}(2kh) = \frac{1}{\sinh(2kh)}$$
$$= \frac{2}{e^{2kh} - e^{-2kh}}$$
$$\simeq \frac{2}{1 + 2kh - (1 - 2kh)} \quad \text{(since } kh \ll 1)$$
$$= \frac{1}{2kh}.$$
Hence,
$$c_g \simeq \tfrac{1}{2}c\left(1 + \frac{2kh}{2kh}\right) = c.$$

(ii) For deep water waves, $\lambda \ll h$, so that $kh \gg 1$. With this approximation,
$$\operatorname{cosech}(2kh) = \frac{1}{\sinh(2kh)}$$
$$= \frac{2}{e^{2kh} - e^{-2kh}}$$
$$\simeq \frac{2}{e^{2kh}} \quad \text{(since } kh \gg 1),$$
and so
$$kh\operatorname{cosech}(2kh) \simeq \frac{2kh}{e^{2kh}} \ll 1.$$
Hence $c_g \simeq \tfrac{1}{2}c$.

Solution 4.4

(a) If shallow water wave theory is used, the group of waves and their envelope travel with the wave speed $50\,\mathrm{m\,s^{-1}}$. Hence, in a day, the group of waves can travel approximately 4320 km.

Since $c = 50 = \sqrt{gh}$, the corresponding depth of ocean is
$$h = \frac{2500}{g} \simeq 255\,\mathrm{m}.$$
The shallow water wave model applies for $h/\lambda \leq \frac{1}{20}$, that is, for $\lambda \geq 20h \simeq 5100\,\mathrm{m}$, so the wavelength should be at least 5.1 km.

(b) If deep water wave theory is used, the group of waves travels with roughly half the wave speed, i.e. with a group velocity of $25\,\mathrm{m\,s^{-1}}$. In a day, the group of waves will travel approximately 2160 km.

Since $c = 50 = \sqrt{\lambda g/(2\pi)}$, the corresponding wavelength is
$$\lambda = \frac{2500 \times 2\pi}{g} \simeq 1600\,\mathrm{m}.$$
The deep water wave model applies for $h/\lambda \geq \frac{1}{2}$, that is, for $h \geq \frac{1}{2}\lambda \simeq 800\,\mathrm{m}$, so the average ocean depth should be at least 800 m.

(For most of a journey across the Atlantic, with an average depth of about 4 km, it is the deep water model that will apply.)

Solution 4.5

(a) The equation of the composite wave is
$$z = \cos(0.9x - 0.975t) + \cos(1.1x - 1.025t)$$
$$= 2\cos(x - t)\cos(0.1(x - 0.25t)).$$
The wave envelope has equations
$$z = \pm 2\cos(0.1(x - 0.25t)).$$
Within the envelope, the wave profile has zeros where $\cos(x - t) = 0$, and it touches the envelope when $\cos(x - t) = \pm 1$.

For $t = 0$, the zeros occur when $\cos x = 0$, that is, when
$$x = \pm\tfrac{1}{2}(2n + 1)\pi \quad (n = 0, 1, 2, \ldots),$$
and the profile touches the envelope when $\cos x = \pm 1$, that is, when
$$x = \pm n\pi \quad (n = 0, 1, 2, \ldots).$$
Since $\cos(x - 2p\pi) = \cos x$ for any integer p, the zeros of the wave profile within the envelope and the points at which it touches the envelope are the same for $t = 2\pi$ and for $t = 4\pi$ as they are (as above) for $t = 0$.

The peak of the wave envelope moves from $x = 0$ at $t = 0$ to $x = \frac{1}{2}\pi$ at $t = 2\pi$ and then to $x = \pi$ at $t = 4\pi$; the distance between its adjacent zeros is $\frac{1}{2} \times 20\pi = 10\pi$ at each time.

The graphs of the three profiles follow overleaf.

Note that the peak of the wave envelope corresponds to wave profile heights 2, 0 and -2, respectively.

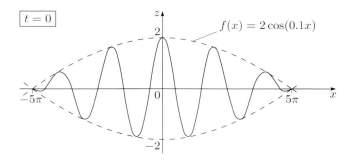

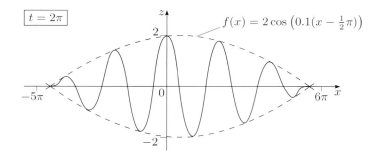

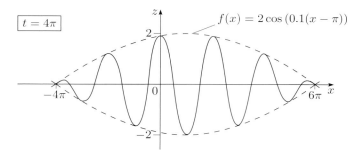

(b) The wave envelope moves to the right with the group velocity, which in this case is 0.25, obtained from the factor $\cos(0.1(x - 0.25t))$. The zeros of the wave profile move to the right with speed 1.0 (from the factor $\cos(x - t)$), and so the peaks within the wave envelope move through the envelope from the back towards the front, i.e. from the left towards the right.

(c) If the two individual waves were $z = \cos(0.9(x - t))$ and $z = \cos(1.1(x - t))$, then each wave would have the same speed 1, so that the wave profile would move along unchanged relative to the wave envelope (which would itself have speed 1).

UNIT 13   Boundary layers and turbulence

Study guide

This unit, on boundary layers and turbulent fluid flow, brings the course to a conclusion. It depends much upon, and refers back to, the basics of fluid mechanics developed in *Units 5–8*.

A facility with manipulations that involve the rules of logarithms, and an understanding of how logarithms are defined, will be of use in Section 4 of the text.

Section 1 has few exercises, since it is mainly intended to set the scene for Sections 2–4, and it should not take too long to complete.

Overall this unit is lengthy, but two subsections within it and most of another may be omitted on a first reading, since they will not be tested in any assessment questions; these are Subsections 2.4, 3.1 and (most of) 3.2. In addition, boxed advice in the margin indicates certain other passages that will not be assessed and hence may be omitted.

Taking this into account, you should find that Sections 2 and 4 take similar times to study, while Section 3 is shorter.

There is no audio activity associated with this unit.

Introduction

This unit follows on from previous ones concerned with modelling fluid flows, namely *Units 5–8*. It was shown in *Unit 6* that a scalar integral form of Euler's equations could model the flow of an idealised fluid, thus relating pressure, speed and body forces. However, in the form given, Bernoulli's equation applied only to an inviscid (frictionless), incompressible fluid. Viscosity was introduced in *Unit 8* to show how real fluid flows are modelled under *laminar* flow conditions. The inclusion of friction meant that a wider range of practical problems could be dealt with. However, since many of the fluid flows encountered in practice involve *turbulent* flow, and not laminar flow, this unit addresses the need to model turbulent fluid flows.

As explained in *Units 7* and *8*, consideration of viscosity can often be confined to a region called the *boundary layer* that is adjacent to any solid surface past which the fluid flows. Outside the boundary layer the flow is essentially inviscid, and so Euler's equations or Bernoulli's equation can be applied. Within the boundary layer, a version of the Navier–Stokes equations for viscous flow is required, and for turbulent flow within a boundary layer, a time-averaged version of the Navier–Stokes equations is called upon.

We shall look at boundary layers for external flow past a flat plate, representing any solid surface whose curvature is not too great, and you will see that the effective thickness of a boundary layer grows with distance along the plate. We also revisit flow within pipes, considered previously in *Unit 8*, where the flow may be thought of as 'all boundary layer'. These situations will be investigated assuming first laminar and then turbulent flow. In each case, values of the *skin friction drag* will be sought. Such calculations are of major importance in practical engineering projects.

See *Unit 8* Subsection 2.3.

Section 1 introduces the topics of boundary layers and turbulence, describing in mainly qualitative terms some of the general features that will be considered in detail later on.

Section 2 deals with boundary layers related to laminar flow, developing the simplified form of the Navier–Stokes equations which applies within boundary layers, and then showing how solutions to these equations can be found in special cases. One outcome is an explanation of how *boundary layer separation* occurs, with its consequence of increased profile drag on the body concerned. The skin friction drag is greater for turbulent than for laminar flows, but as you will see, this is sometimes compensated for by lower profile drag.

Section 3 takes the first steps in modelling turbulent flow. This starts by placing the Navier–Stokes equations on a firmer footing, by showing in general how the shear stresses caused by viscosity are related to velocity derivatives according to the Newtonian model. It turns out that the *turbulence* (seemingly random and chaotic fluctuations to the flow) can be modelled, in terms of its effect on the mean velocity, as providing further (and much larger) shear stresses known as *Reynolds stresses*. These terms become apparent after undertaking a suitable averaging process with the Navier–Stokes equations, but the Reynolds stresses require further modelling before any solution to the Navier–Stokes equations can be looked for.

Section 4 analyses the velocity profile for turbulent flow in a boundary layer, over a plate or within a pipe, but increasingly concentrating on pipes. This culminates in an explanation of how to work out the *skin friction coefficient* (and hence the skin friction drag) in a pipe, given values for the Reynolds number and for a numerical coefficient that indicates the *roughness* of the pipe wall.

For ease of reference, the following table gives standard values for the density, ρ, coefficient of viscosity, μ, and *kinematic viscosity, $\nu = \mu/\rho$*, for air and water.

Table 0.1   Values of physical constants for air and water

fluid	ρ $(\mathrm{kg\,m^{-3}})$	μ $(\mathrm{kg\,m^{-1}\,s^{-1}})$	ν $(\mathrm{m^2\,s^{-1}})$
air	1.20	1.80×10^{-5}	1.50×10^{-5}
water	1.00×10^3	1.00×10^{-3}	1.00×10^{-6}

The units for μ may also be written as Pa s.

1 Overview

1.1 Boundary layers

It is not possible to solve Euler's equations for fluid flow in a region which has a solid boundary, where the no-slip condition applies, together with a specified non-zero flow velocity or pressure gradient at some distance from the boundary. However, it is often the case that Euler's equations describe such a flow very well provided that the solid boundary is not approached too closely, and when these equations for inviscid flow can be applied, it is convenient to do so. Near enough to the boundary the shear stresses due to viscosity are important, even when the coefficient of viscosity μ is small, so it is never valid to take the limit as $\mu \to 0$ in the immediate vicinity of a solid surface.

This was demonstrated when considering the fluid injection flow of *Unit 8* Subsection 3.1. The fluid here is assumed to be viscous.

It follows, as was first pointed out by Ludwig Prandtl in 1904, that in order to describe the flow completely we need to consider particularly what happens in a thin *boundary layer* between the solid surface and the rest of the fluid. This is illustrated schematically for two-dimensional flow past an aerofoil, with a uniform incoming stream, in Figure 1.1(a).

This is also the limit as $Re \to \infty$, where Re is the Reynolds number.

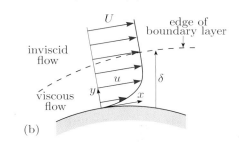

(a)   (b)

Figure 1.1

The **boundary layer** is defined as that layer within which the influence of the solid surface is apparent, although as you will see, this definition may pose some difficulties when examined in detail. As indicated in Figure 1.1(a), the thickness of the boundary layer, denoted by δ, gradually increases along the solid surface. Figure 1.1(b) shows the situation in close-up, with x measuring distance along the surface and y directed normal to the surface at each point. The velocity profile u for given x, regarded as a function of y, increases from zero at the solid boundary to the free stream velocity U at the edge of the boundary layer, where $y = \delta(x)$. Outside the boundary layer the flow is regarded as inviscid, with a velocity $u = U(x)$, whereas within the boundary layer the Navier–Stokes equations apply and $u = u(x, y)$, with $u(x, 0) = 0$ and $u(x, \delta) = U(x)$. The situation is shown again in Figure 1.2, where the solid surface has been 'straightened out'.

In fact, flows typical of boundary layers can also be found in the absence of an adjacent solid surface, but we do not consider such cases here.

Note the use here of a half-arrowhead to indicate the shear stress at the boundary.

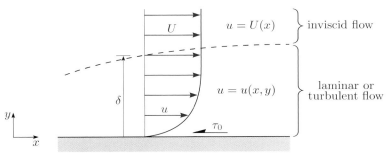

Figure 1.2

Flow past a flat plate, with the incoming stream parallel to the plate, will be considered in considerable detail during this unit. The origin of coordinates is usually taken at the leading edge of the plate, which is where the boundary layer starts to form. The flow within the boundary layer may be laminar or turbulent, and both will be considered later. According to Newton's model of viscosity, there is a shear stress

$$\tau = \mu \frac{\partial u}{\partial y} \tag{1.1}$$

for a laminar flow throughout the boundary layer. The shear stress at the boundary is denoted by τ_0, as indicated in Figure 1.2. For turbulent flow there is a larger shear stress across most of the boundary layer, which is not described by Equation (1.1).

The boundary layer velocity profiles, shown in Figures 1.1 and 1.2, may change significantly with distance along the surface. If the inviscid flow in the external region is moving against an adverse pressure gradient, then the velocity profile within the boundary layer may alter in the manner shown in Figure 1.3.

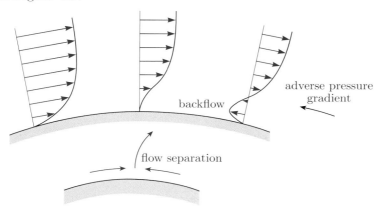

backflow

adverse pressure gradient

flow separation

Figure 1.3

This involves a change in the sign of $[\partial u/\partial y]_{y=0}$, which is initially positive. Once this becomes negative, there is a backflow very close to the plate, and *flow separation* has occurred. The point of separation is where $[\partial u/\partial y]_{y=0} = 0$. Flow separation causes large *profile drag*, since it effectively increases the width of the body past which the stream flows. The region beyond the separation point and close to the boundary is filled with vortices and is at low pressure. Both laminar and turbulent boundary layers can separate in this way, but laminar boundary layers are more prone to do so.

1.2 Turbulence

In everyday usage, the word 'turbulence' describes a disturbed state of a system involving movements which are random or hard to predict. Within fluid mechanics, **turbulence** is a three-dimensional, time-dependent, eddying motion with many different length scales, causing continuous mixing of the fluid.

It is possible to abstract from the turbulent flow a simpler *mean* flow, by averaging the perturbations of the eddying motion over a suitable short time interval. Suppose, for example, that Figure 1.4 represents graphically the three components of a turbulent flow with velocity $\mathbf{u} = u\,\mathbf{i} + v\,\mathbf{j} + w\,\mathbf{k}$, at a particular point.

This is often called flow past a flat plate at *zero incidence*.

Laminar flow, or flow in layers, was considered in *Unit 8*.

See Equation (1.4) of *Unit 8*. Here we use y in place of z.

Profile drag was mentioned in *Unit 7* Subsection 5.1.

Previously in the course we denoted the components of $\mathbf{u}$ by u_1, u_2, u_3. In this unit, subscripts will be used for other purposes.

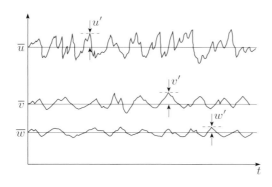

Figure 1.4

Each component fluctuates about a mean value, denoted by $\overline{u}$, $\overline{v}$, $\overline{w}$, respectively. We write

$$u = \overline{u} + u', \qquad v = \overline{v} + v', \qquad w = \overline{w} + w', \tag{1.2}$$

where u', v', w' are the turbulent perturbations relative to the respective mean values. Clearly the flow is not steady, but if $\overline{u}$, $\overline{v}$ and $\overline{w}$ do not alter with time, as shown in Figure 1.4, then it is called *quasi-steady*. If the flow is not quasi-steady, the changes in $\overline{u}$, $\overline{v}$ and $\overline{w}$ with time will still occur much more slowly than the changes involved in the perturbations u', v' and w'.

The averaging process is explained further in Subsection 3.2.

The primes used here denote turbulent perturbations, and *not* derivatives.

In reality, where turbulent flow occurs, there are always perturbations in all three spatial dimensions, even if the mean flow is two-dimensional. Only for modelling purposes can two-dimensional turbulent perturbations be imagined. As Figure 1.4 illustrates, turbulence is *anisotropic*; that is, the average magnitudes of the perturbation components in the x-, y- and z-directions need not be the same.

By the definition of the perturbations in Equation (1.2), we have $\overline{u'} = \overline{v'} = \overline{w'} = 0$. In order to measure and compare the sizes of perturbation components, we need to consider the quantities

$$\sqrt{\overline{u'^2}}, \qquad \sqrt{\overline{v'^2}}, \qquad \sqrt{\overline{w'^2}},$$

which will always be non-zero if there are turbulent perturbations present. We can also consider expressions such as $\overline{u'v'}$; in fact, you will see that $-\rho\,\overline{u'v'}$ can be interpreted as the turbulent shear stress, which replaces the right-hand side of Equation (1.1) throughout most of a turbulent boundary layer.

Note that
$$\overline{u'v'} \neq \overline{u'}\,\overline{v'} = 0.$$

Figure 1.5 (overleaf), which is based on experimental measurements, shows how the dimensionless quantities

$$\frac{\sqrt{\overline{u'^2}}}{U}, \qquad \frac{\sqrt{\overline{v'^2}}}{U}, \qquad \frac{\sqrt{\overline{w'^2}}}{U},$$

where U is the free stream velocity, vary across a turbulent boundary layer. Here u' is in the direction of flow, v' is normal to the plate surface and w' is in the third coordinate direction. This demonstrates, as claimed above, that turbulence is anisotropic.

The inset graph shows, to different scales, how the quantities vary close to the boundary at $y = 0$.

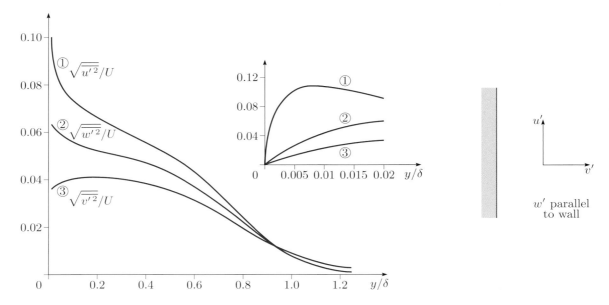

Figure 1.5

Turbulence is important because it can transport large amounts of momentum (and also other physical quantities, such as heat) even when the mean flow is steady. Figure 1.6 shows an imaginary interface (the broken line) between regions of higher velocity above and lower velocity below. There is no mean flow from one side of the interface to the other, but particles crossing the interface within turbulent fluctuations will, on average, tend to transport higher momentum from above to below, and lower momentum from below to above. On average, therefore, the turbulence causes a net transfer of momentum from the upper to the lower region, which has the same effect as if the upper region of fluid were pulling the lower fluid forwards. This is the same effect as that caused by a shear stress, and so turbulence causes an effective shear stress on the mean motion, known as the *Reynolds stress*. Except very close to the solid boundary, this swamps the effect of the viscous shear stress given by Equation (1.1).

Figure 1.6

Turbulence creates eddies at various length scales, containing significant amounts of vorticity and extracting energy from the mean flow. The size of the eddies varies depending also on distance from any solid boundary. The larger eddies pass energy down to progressively smaller eddies, and eventually to eddies which are small enough for their energy to be dissipated by the action of viscosity. Hence turbulence features an energy cascade, with energy produced in the large eddies and dissipated from the very small ones. This is summed up in a memorable couplet by L.F. Richardson (1920):

Statistical analysis of experimental results reveals a whole spectrum of eddy sizes, at different spatial and temporal scales.

> Big whorls have little whorls,
> That feed on their velocity;
> And little whorls have lesser whorls,
> And so on to viscosity.

This quotation is a parody of a couplet from Augustus de Morgan, concerning fleas, which is itself based on lines by Jonathan Swift.

Turbulence is worthy of much attention because it lies at the heart of many practical problems in engineering and other fields. Turbulent fluid flows occur in practice much more widely than laminar flows, and so some understanding of turbulent flow is a prerequisite for the mathematical modelling of real fluid motion. Despite their relative complexity, models incorporating turbulence can be implemented within computational fluid dynamics (CFD).

Turbulence manifests itself in many ways in everyday life. It causes irregular motion for aircraft in flight, provokes gusts of wind, and changes the pattern of clouds. It is also present in the wakes shed from cars and high-speed trains, telephone wires and chimney stacks. It diffuses pollutants and sediment in rivers, and enhances heat transfer.

Its role in governing velocity distributions and resistance to fluid motion has a significant impact on the natural world. For example, if rivers flowed only under laminar conditions, then the resistance to flow would be much lower, and water speeds would be orders of magnitude higher than they are. This would greatly increase sediment motion, changing the whole topography of the Earth's surface.

It should be emphasised that, despite the complexity of the motion, turbulent flow can be modelled validly by the Navier–Stokes equations (leading to the CFD method known as direct numerical simulation, DNS). However, the Navier–Stokes equations can equally describe laminar flows over the same solution domain and with the same initial and boundary conditions. This is so because, owing to the non-linearity of the differential equations, solutions of the Navier–Stokes equations are not unique. Additional information concerning the nature of the turbulence is therefore required before a unique solution can be pinned down.

Given the complex and chaotic nature of turbulence, it is a challenging topic of study. Similarly, experimental measurements of turbulent flow pose significant problems and require great ingenuity. Typically, in order to understand a turbulent flow structure, we require simultaneous measurements of the high-frequency fluctuations in velocity and pressure, and perhaps also of sediment concentration and temperature, at various points in the fluid flow. Most of these parameters are measured by indirect methods, which there is not space to describe here. Ideally, measurement methods should be non-invasive, allowing for accurate parameter values to be obtained without affecting the flow at measurement points. The output from experiments typically requires large amounts of statistical analysis to be carried out by computer. On the other hand, given the rapid changes of variables involved, CFD simulations of turbulent fluid flow may require very large amounts of computer time, even on modern machines.

Progress in the understanding of turbulence has always depended on advances in experimental techniques. It is not surprising that this progress has been somewhat slow. In 1932 the fluid dynamicist Sir Horace Lamb reflected the perceived difficulty of the subject by speaking as follows to an audience of scientists:

The first edition of Lamb's classic book *Hydrodynamics* was published in 1879. The sixth edition (1932) is still in print at the time of writing.

> I am an old man now, and when I die and go to heaven there are two matters on which I hope for enlightenment. One is quantum electrodynamics, and the other is the turbulent motion of fluids. And about the former I am rather optimistic.
>
> Moin, P. and Kim, J. 'Tackling turbulence with supercomputers',
> *Scientific American*, January 1997.

1.3   From laminar to turbulent flow

Flow in pipes

In classic experiments performed at Manchester University in 1883, Osborne Reynolds demonstrated for the first time the physical characteristics of turbulence and the precise conditions for its onset for flow within pipes. He showed in the process that there is a clear distinction between laminar and turbulent flow.

Reynolds also developed the RANS equations, as described in Subsection 3.2.

Figure 1.7 is a sketch of Reynolds' apparatus for the experiments, taken from his 1883 paper, and Figure 1.8 shows this apparatus in schematic form, together with an impression of the dye traces that were observed as the volume flow rate within the pipe was increased.

Figure 1.7

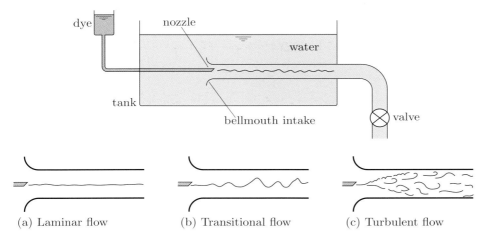

(a) Laminar flow   (b) Transitional flow   (c) Turbulent flow

Note the 'triangle' of line segments in Figure 1.8, used to denote a free liquid surface.

Figure 1.8

At low water velocities, dye released into the central region of the pipe emerged as a single thread and continued as such for the entire length of the pipe, as shown in Figure 1.8(a). As the velocity was increased, perturbations were observed in the dye thread (see Figure 1.8(b)), indicating a velocity component transverse to the main motion and fluctuating. At higher velocities still, complete mixing took place (see Figure 1.8(c)), indicating a much higher level of transverse fluctuations.

Reynolds also observed that, while the dye thread broke up into turbulent flow at some distance from the entrance to the pipe, further increases in velocity caused successive shifts in the point of break-up towards the pipe entrance.

He was able to deduce from his experiments (with pipes of three different diameters) that the transition from laminar to turbulent flow depended on the degree of disturbance at the entrance to the pipe and also on the quantity now known as the Reynolds number, Re. For pipe flow, this is defined as

$$Re = \frac{\rho U d}{\mu} = \frac{U d}{\nu},$$

where U is the mean flow velocity and d is the diameter of the pipe. We write $\nu = \mu/\rho$, where ρ is the density of the fluid and μ is its coefficient of viscosity, to define the *kinematic viscosity, ν*. This is much used later in the unit, and allows one symbol to be written in place of two. To distinguish it from ν, the coefficient μ is sometimes called the *dynamic viscosity*.

The units of ν, as you can check from those for μ and ρ, are $\mathrm{m^2\,s^{-1}}$.

In Reynolds' words, his deduction was as follows:

> The general character of the motion of fluids in contact with solid surfaces depends on the relation between a physical constant of the fluid and the product of the linear dimensions of the space occupied by the fluid and the velocity.

> Reynolds, O. (1883), *Phil. Trans. R. Soc. London*, 1 January, vol. 174, pp. 935–982.

Values for ρ, μ and ν for air and water are given at the end of the Introduction.

For flows at less than a critical value of Re, the flow is laminar, whereas a higher value of Re corresponds to turbulent flow. The critical value of Re for pipes is often taken to be 2300, and we shall choose that value here. However, there is dispute among practitioners about which single value of Re should be regarded as the critical value, and many prefer to take 2000. The fact of the matter is that the 'degree of disturbance at the entrance to the pipe' has an important bearing on the result, as also does any vibration which may be experienced by the apparatus as a whole. By keeping such disturbances to a minimum, Reynolds was able to push the experimentally determined value of Re up to almost 13 000. However, although his apparatus is still in working order in Manchester University, the critical value for Re that can be obtained from it now is much reduced, owing to the background level of vibration induced by city traffic.

Fully turbulent flow occurs after a transitional region, usually taken as

$$2300 < Re < 4000.$$

Exercise 1.1

(a) Calculate the Reynolds number for flow with mean velocity $U = 0.5\,\mathrm{m\,s^{-1}}$ in a domestic water pipe of diameter 12 mm.

For water, take $\nu = 1.0 \times 10^{-6}\,\mathrm{m^2\,s^{-1}}$.

(b) Show that the flow is turbulent. Below what value for U would the flow be laminar?

Exercise 1.2

Find the volume flow rate at which the flow in a pipe of diameter 5 mm would change from laminar to turbulent, if the pipe were carrying

(a) water;   (b) air.

Give your answers in litres per second ($\mathrm{l\,s^{-1}}$), where 1 litre $= 10^{-3}\,\mathrm{m^3}$. For water, take $\nu = 1.0 \times 10^{-6}\,\mathrm{m^2\,s^{-1}}$. For air, take $\nu = 1.5 \times 10^{-5}\,\mathrm{m^2\,s^{-1}}$.

A second classic experiment performed by Reynolds concerned the relationship between the pressure drop within a pipe and the flow rate. The volume flow rate was varied from a low value, at which the flow was laminar, to a much higher value, at which turbulent flow occurred. The resulting relationship between measured head drop Δh and mean velocity U in the pipe is

$$\frac{\Delta h}{L} = KU^n, \tag{1.3}$$

where L is the length of pipe over which the head drop is measured. A log-log plot of this relationship is sketched in Figure 1.9.

If p is the pressure, then $h = p/(\rho g)$ is the corresponding *head*.

The parameter K is a function of U which has a constant value for laminar flow (with $n = 1$) and tends to a limit for large U, corresponding to $n = 2$.

The power n is the slope of this graph.

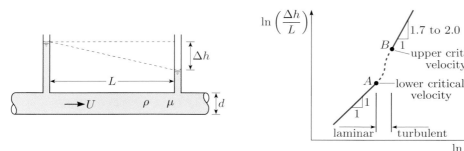

Figure 1.9

In laminar flow ($Re < 2300$), Equation (1.3) gives a linear relationship between Δh and U ($n = 1.0$), whereas in fully turbulent flow ($Re > 4000$), the relationship is non-linear, with n between 1.7 and 2.0.

The proportionality for laminar flow was predicted by the Hagen–Poiseuille formula in *Unit 8* Subsection 2.3.

The demarcation between laminar and turbulent flow is again clear, as is the transition from one to the other. The form of Equation (1.3) is predicted by the *Darcy–Weisbach equation*, which you will see in Subsection 2.5, together with information from Section 4 about the *skin friction coefficient*, c_f. In a pipe, c_f is defined by $c_f = \tau_0/(\frac{1}{2}\rho U^2)$, where τ_0 is the shear stress at the wall and U is the mean velocity.

Note from this definition that c_f is dimensionless.

Both τ_0 and c_f vary with Re, and do so in a different way for laminar and turbulent flows. Figure 1.10 shows how $\lambda = 4c_f$ varies with Re, across a full range of values of Re, for smooth-walled pipes. You will see how this graph arises in Subsection 4.2.

The *Darcy friction factor*, λ, is much used by engineers.

From knowledge of c_f (or λ), the drag force F_L over a length L of pipe can be calculated as

$$F_L = \pi dL\tau_0 = \tfrac{1}{2}\pi d\,c_f\rho LU^2.$$

The value of τ_0 is constant within the pipe, since the flow is fully developed.

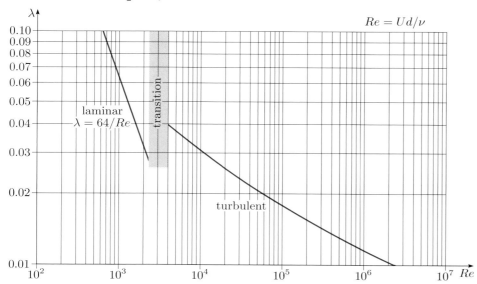

Figure 1.10

The formatting of the graph in Figure 1.10 is worthy of note, since on both axes it features scales which are linear logarithmically but non-linear according to the values actually marked. In other words, the graphical information would be identical if presented above a horizontal axis marked in either of the ways (a) or (b) shown in Figure 1.11. Similar formatting of diagrams will be seen later.

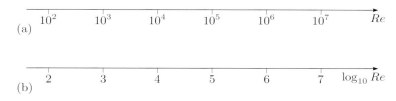

Figure 1.11

The unmarked vertical lines in Figure 1.10 show equal increments of Re; for example, the unmarked lines to the right of that for $Re = 10^3$ indicate the values 2×10^3, 3×10^3, ..., 9×10^3.

Figure 1.10 is also noteworthy in that it describes a relationship between dimensionless variables, $\lambda = 4c_f = 8\tau_0/(\rho U^2)$ and $Re = Ud/\nu$. Equations that relate dimensionless variables have wider application than those which do not, and you will see many instances of dimensionless quantities being related later in the unit.

External flow past a boundary

In the case of flow past an external boundary such as a flat plate, both laminar and turbulent flow occur. Figure 1.12 shows the general structure of the boundary layer on a flat plate. Whatever the state of the incoming flow (laminar or turbulent), a laminar boundary layer develops above the plate, starting from the leading edge. However, if the plate is long enough, a transition occurs following which the flow in the boundary layer is turbulent.

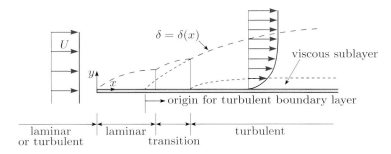

Figure 1.12

A turbulent boundary layer grows thicker more rapidly than a laminar one, so that the boundary layer bulges outwards after transition. Also the skin friction drag on the plate increases more rapidly in a turbulent boundary layer, and so overall skin friction drag is increased by an early transition.

The Reynolds number in this case is defined as

$$Re_x = \frac{Ux}{\nu},$$

where ν is the kinematic viscosity of the fluid, U is the exterior stream velocity, and x is the distance along the plate from the leading edge. So in this case, the 'characteristic length' in the Reynolds number definition is a variable quantity. Just as 2300 (approximately) is a critical value of the (differently specified) Reynolds number for flow within a pipe, so too there

This is the first instance of several in the unit for which a subscript is added to Re to indicate which Reynolds number is involved. In some cases there will be more than one possible choice for 'the Reynolds number'.

67

is a critical value of Re_x at which laminar flow turns to turbulent flow after a transition. This is usually taken as $Re_x = 5 \times 10^5$, though again considerable variation in this figure is observed owing to external factors.

Suppose, for example, that air flows at a stream speed of $10 \, \mathrm{m \, s^{-1}}$ past a flat plate. Since the kinematic viscosity of air is $\nu = 1.5 \times 10^{-5} \, \mathrm{m^2 \, s^{-1}}$, transition from a laminar to a turbulent boundary layer will take place at a distance x from the leading edge of the plate, where

$$5 \times 10^5 = \frac{10x}{1.5 \times 10^{-5}}; \qquad \text{that is,} \qquad x = 0.75 \, \mathrm{m}.$$

If this calculation is performed once more for water flowing past the plate, with $\nu = 1.0 \times 10^{-6} \, \mathrm{m^2 \, s^{-1}}$, then transition is predicted to take place at $x = 0.05 \, \mathrm{m}$, which is much closer to the leading edge.

For a given external flow speed, a boundary layer will be purely laminar over a flat plate only if the length of the plate is less than the value of x at which transition takes place; otherwise, turbulence inevitably occurs. Since the point of transition is given by the value of x for which $Ux/\nu = 5 \times 10^5$, it follows that *increasing* the incoming stream speed U will *decrease* the distance x from the leading edge at which transition occurs. For a long plate, it is often a reasonable approximation to assume that the boundary layer is turbulent along its whole length.

An interesting feature of turbulent boundary layers, included in Figure 1.12, is that there remains a very narrow region at the inside of the boundary layer for which viscous shear stresses are comparable to or greater than the turbulent stresses, and some laminar flow occurs. This is due to the close presence of the solid boundary, and the region is called the *viscous sublayer*.

In reality, the transition from laminar to turbulent flow does not take place above just one point on the plate but over a short range of values of x, as Figure 1.12 indicates. However, this range becomes shorter with increases in U.

For a boundary layer over a flat plate, the skin friction coefficient c_f again takes the form $\tau_0/(\frac{1}{2}\rho U^2)$, but (as for the Reynolds number) the velocity U here is the external stream velocity, and not the mean velocity that is used in the case of pipes. For external flow, both τ_0 and c_f vary as functions of x (whereas in fully developed pipe flow they are constant). The graph of c_f against Re_x has the same general form as that shown in Figure 1.10. A *total skin friction coefficient*, C_L, is defined by averaging c_f over the length L of the plate, to give

$$C_L = \frac{1}{L} \int_0^L c_f \, dx.$$

This is equivalent to

$$C_L = \frac{F_L}{\frac{1}{2}\rho U^2 L}, \qquad \text{where} \qquad F_L = \int_0^L \tau_0 \, dx$$

is the total drag force per unit breadth due to skin friction acting on the plate.

Consider now an incoming steady flow around an object such as a sphere or cylinder. It was remarked in Subsection 1.1 that in the presence of an adverse external pressure gradient the boundary layer may separate, causing a great increase in profile drag, and that separation occurs more readily for laminar than for turbulent boundary layers. Following from this, it is often beneficial to provoke the transition from laminar to turbulent flow at an earlier stage than it would otherwise occur, since the

For a given pipe and fluid, the fully developed flow will be laminar throughout or turbulent throughout, as determined by the value of U. The flow over a plate, on the other hand, will always (unless the plate is too short) be *first* laminar and *then* turbulent, with changes to U altering the point of transition.

This is similar to one of the effects noted by Reynolds in his experiments on pipe flow, in the region before the flow became fully developed.

Some authors write c_{fm} rather than c_f for a skin friction coefficient that depends on a mean velocity.

Such an 'adverse external pressure gradient' occurs over the back half of a sphere or cylinder, after the external stream speed has reached its maximum at the widest point of the body.

turbulent boundary layer will stay attached to the body for longer than the laminar boundary layer. While doing this *increases* the overall skin friction drag, it dramatically *decreases* the profile drag. Such a 'provocation' of the laminar/turbulent transition can be brought about by unevenness or protrusions on the surface. The dimples on golf balls have this effect of provoking an early onset of turbulence, resulting in less overall drag on the balls.

See the *Media Guide* for more about the topics in Section 1.

Choice of shape, by streamlining of the boundary, is also important in preventing boundary layer separation. To see how significant these considerations are, Figure 1.13 shows cross-sections of a cylinder and streamlined aerofoil shape which experience the same overall drag for the same incoming stream velocity. The length of the aerofoil is 167 times the diameter of the cylinder, but because of careful shaping, the boundary layer on the aerofoil remains laminar and attached for almost the entire length, and so its profile drag is kept very small.

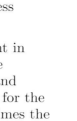

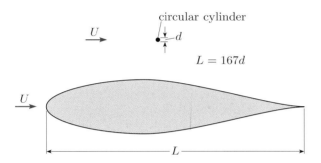

Figure 1.13

To conclude this section, consider Figure 1.14, which shows as a function of $Re = Ud/\nu$ the *overall drag coefficient*

$$C_D = \frac{F_D}{\frac{1}{2}\rho U^2 A}$$

on a cylinder of diameter d, where F_D is the total drag force, U is the incoming stream speed, and A is the projected frontal area of the cylinder.

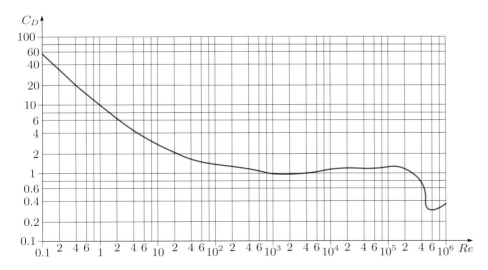

Figure 1.14

It is noticeable that at around $Re = 4 \times 10^5$ there is a sudden and significant drop in the value of C_D, corresponding to a large decrease in overall drag. This may be explained as follows.

At smaller values of Re, the boundary layer is laminar until the point at which it separates from the cylinder, because the transition point to turbulent flow, calculated much as described earlier for a flat plate, is located further along the cylinder's surface. Increasing U (and hence Re) has the effect of moving this point forwards, and from about $Re = 4 \times 10^5$ upwards, the transition point has advanced ahead of the laminar boundary layer separation point. Hence separation at that point is inhibited, and takes place only much later, with the effect that can be seen in reducing the drag.

While Sections 2–4 deal with boundary layers and turbulence in much greater detail, it may be helpful to bear in mind some of the general features that have been described in this section.

2   Laminar boundary layers

This section analyses how boundary layers behave when the flow is laminar. The analysis applies mainly to flow past a flat plate, though it generalises to an extent to other surfaces. The special form of the Navier–Stokes equations which applies in a boundary layer is developed in Subsection 2.1, and an integral form of the boundary layer equations is obtained in Subsection 2.2, together with some approximate solutions. An exact solution in a particular case is found in Subsection 2.3. The topic of boundary layer separation is discussed in Subsection 2.4, while Subsection 2.5 recalls the exact solutions of the Navier–Stokes equations that apply for laminar flow in uniform pipes and channels.

2.1   The boundary layer equations

Consider a steady two-dimensional flow of an incompressible fluid in the (x, y)-plane, without body forces, which has velocity field $\mathbf{u} = u\,\mathbf{i} + v\,\mathbf{j}$. For this flow the continuity equation is

The velocity components in this unit are taken as u, v, w, rather than u_1, u_2, u_3 as in previous units.

$$\frac{\partial u}{\partial x} + \frac{\partial v}{\partial y} = 0, \tag{2.1}$$

and the Navier–Stokes equations are

See Equations (2.2) of *Unit 8*.

$$\rho \left(u\frac{\partial u}{\partial x} + v\frac{\partial u}{\partial y} \right) = -\frac{\partial p}{\partial x} + \mu \left(\frac{\partial^2 u}{\partial x^2} + \frac{\partial^2 u}{\partial y^2} \right), \tag{2.2}$$

$$\rho \left(u\frac{\partial v}{\partial x} + v\frac{\partial v}{\partial y} \right) = -\frac{\partial p}{\partial y} + \mu \left(\frac{\partial^2 v}{\partial x^2} + \frac{\partial^2 v}{\partial y^2} \right). \tag{2.3}$$

The fluid flows past a fixed flat plate, whose cross-section is taken as the positive x-axis, as shown in Figure 2.1. While the flow passes on either side of the plate, we shall consider flow past the top face of the plate only.

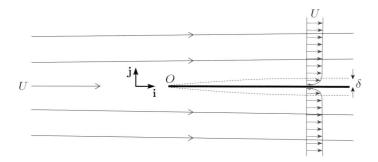

Figure 2.1

For $x < 0$, the flow is uniform with $\mathbf{u} = U\,\mathbf{i}$. The effect of the plate on the x-component of the velocity profile is shown in Figure 2.1. Due to the no-slip condition, u varies from zero at the plate to the free stream value U at some distance from the plate. This change takes place across a small distance δ, perpendicular to the plate, which is observed to grow as x increases; that is, $\delta = \delta(x)$ is an increasing function. The plate has finite extent to the right (being of length L, say), and the *boundary layer* defined by $y \le \delta$ is very small by comparison, so that $\delta \ll L$.

To analyse this situation, the first step is to make Equations (2.2) and (2.3) dimensionless, by putting

$$x^* = \frac{x}{L}, \quad y^* = \frac{y}{\delta}, \quad u^* = \frac{u}{U}, \quad v^* = \frac{vL}{U\delta}, \quad p^* = \frac{p}{\rho U^2}.$$

This gives

$$\frac{\delta^2}{L^2}\left(u^*\frac{\partial u^*}{\partial x^*} + v^*\frac{\partial u^*}{\partial y^*}\right) = -\frac{\delta^2}{L^2}\frac{\partial p^*}{\partial x^*} + \frac{\mu}{\rho L U}\left(\frac{\delta^2}{L^2}\frac{\partial^2 u^*}{\partial x^{*2}} + \frac{\partial^2 u^*}{\partial y^{*2}}\right), \quad (2.4)$$

$$\frac{\delta^2}{L^2}\left(u^*\frac{\partial v^*}{\partial x^*} + v^*\frac{\partial v^*}{\partial y^*}\right) = -\frac{\partial p^*}{\partial y^*} + \frac{\mu}{\rho L U}\left(\frac{\delta^2}{L^2}\frac{\partial^2 v^*}{\partial x^{*2}} + \frac{\partial^2 v^*}{\partial y^{*2}}\right). \quad (2.5)$$

It follows from Equation (2.4), since $\delta \ll L$, that the term involving $\partial^2 u^*/\partial x^{*2}$ is negligible compared with that for $\partial^2 u^*/\partial y^{*2}$. The remaining terms can be regarded as having a comparable order of magnitude *provided* that the Reynolds number $Re = \rho L U/\mu$ is large, so that

$$\frac{\delta}{L} = O\left(Re^{-1/2}\right). \quad (2.6)$$

This gives a rough indication of what thickness the boundary layer may be expected to have for a given Reynolds number, and also suggests that the boundary layer may become narrower (smaller δ) for a larger value of Re.

Applying Equation (2.6) to Equation (2.5), and neglecting terms of order δ^2/L^2 or Re^{-1}, gives

$$0 = -\frac{\partial p^*}{\partial y^*}.$$

The corresponding dimensional form $\partial p/\partial y = 0$ indicates that $p = p(x)$. Hence within the boundary layer, Equations (2.2) and (2.3) reduce to the single equation

$$u\frac{\partial u}{\partial x} + v\frac{\partial u}{\partial y} = -\frac{1}{\rho}\frac{dp}{dx} + \frac{\mu}{\rho}\frac{\partial^2 u}{\partial y^2}. \quad (2.7)$$

Also the continuity equation still applies:

$$\frac{\partial u}{\partial x} + \frac{\partial v}{\partial y} = 0. \quad (2.1)$$

For the moment, take δ to be the boundary layer thickness at the trailing edge of the plate, that is, $\delta(L)$.

Equations (2.4) and (2.5) are obtained in a very similar manner to Equations (4.3) and (4.4) for the slider bearing problem in *Unit 8*, with δ, y, u, v, ρU^2 respectively in place of h_1, z, u_1, u_3, P. The outcome is different, however, because different assumptions are made here.

71

The derivation of Equation (2.7) has taken no account of the nature of the external flow, for which the effects of viscosity are assumed to be negligible. Hence Euler's equation and Bernoulli's equation can be applied to the external flow.

The derivation for a flat plate may appear to be for rather a specialised situation. However, it is possible to show that Equations (2.1) and (2.7) also apply to curved surfaces, provided that the curvature is not too great. For this purpose, it is necessary to choose coordinates x, y such that x measures distance along the surface in the direction of flow, while y is always measured normal to the local surface direction, as indicated in Figure 2.2.

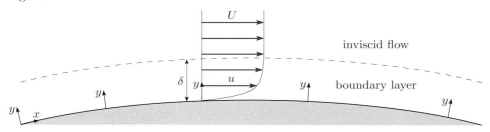

Figure 2.2

The motion of fluid close to such a curved surface will have a centripetal acceleration of order U^2/R, where R is the radius of curvature of the surface. The pressure gradient $\partial p/\partial y$ required to maintain this acceleration is of the order of $\rho U^2/R$, corresponding to a dimensionless pressure gradient $\partial p^*/\partial y^* = O(\delta/R)$. Hence it is still reasonable to take $\partial p/\partial y = 0$ if $\delta \ll R$.

Given flow past a curved surface, the external flow speed may vary along the surface, that is, $U = U(x)$.

Taking the limit of Equation (2.2) as y becomes large (compared to δ), for which $u \to U$, $\partial u/\partial y \to 0$ and the viscous term is neglected, gives

$$\rho U \frac{dU}{dx} = -\frac{dp}{dx}. \tag{2.8}$$

Applying this result to Equation (2.7), the **boundary layer equations** may be written as

$$\frac{\partial u}{\partial x} + \frac{\partial v}{\partial y} = 0, \tag{2.1}$$

$$u\frac{\partial u}{\partial x} + v\frac{\partial u}{\partial y} = U\frac{dU}{dx} + \nu\frac{\partial^2 u}{\partial y^2}, \tag{2.9}$$

where $\nu = \mu/\rho$ is the *kinematic viscosity* of the fluid.

See the *Media Guide* for more on the derivation of the boundary layer equations.

This can also be deduced from Bernoulli's equation applied outside the boundary layer.

To distinguish it from ν, the coefficient of viscosity μ is often called the *dynamic viscosity*.

Boundary conditions

At the surface of the plate, where $y = 0$, we have the condition $\mathbf{u} = \mathbf{0}$, or

$$u = v = 0 \quad \text{at } y = 0.$$

The solution within the boundary layer must also be matched up with the external flow, so that $u \to U$ as y becomes large. Hence also all derivatives $\partial u/\partial y$, $\partial^2 u/\partial y^2$, etc. tend to zero as y becomes large.

From the second derivative upwards, these zero limit values for large y follow from Equation (2.9) and derivatives of it, so need not be specified as separate conditions. Also $\partial u/\partial y \to 0$ as $y \to \infty$ is a consequence of $u \to U$ as $y \to \infty$, and so the latter is the only independent boundary condition needed for $y \to \infty$. This situation alters (as below) when an artificial finite limit is placed on the extent of the boundary layer.

Exercise 2.1

(a) Deduce from the boundary condition at the surface and from the continuity equation (2.1) that

$$\frac{\partial u}{\partial x} = \frac{\partial v}{\partial x} = \frac{\partial v}{\partial y} = 0 \quad \text{at } y = 0.$$

(b) Show that

$$-U\frac{dU}{dx} = \nu \left[\frac{\partial^2 u}{\partial y^2}\right]_{y=0} = \frac{1}{\rho}\left[\frac{\partial \tau}{\partial y}\right]_{y=0},$$

where $\tau = \mu\, \partial u/\partial y$ is the shear stress (for a Newtonian fluid) in the x-direction.

While there is in fact no hard and fast position at which the boundary layer ends, in the direction outwards from the surface, it is often convenient to assume a finite boundary layer thickness $\delta(x)$, for which the 'matching' boundary conditions become

$$u\left(x, \delta(x)\right) = U(x), \qquad \frac{\partial u}{\partial y}\left(x, \delta(x)\right) = 0, \qquad \frac{\partial^2 u}{\partial y^2}\left(x, \delta(x)\right) = 0.$$

Any solution for these boundary conditions would only be an approximation to the exact boundary layer flow, but could be a good approximation if δ is sufficiently large. A common choice for the 'finite thickness' of a real boundary layer is where the boundary layer flow velocity attains 99% of the free stream value.

2.2   The momentum integral equation

Before considering solutions of the boundary layer equations (2.1) and (2.9), we first derive an integral form of these equations. It follows from the continuity equation (2.1) and the boundary condition $v(x,0)=0$ that if $h > 0$ then

There is no need to follow the detail of these manipulations, which lead to Equations (2.13) to (2.15).

$$v(x,h) = \int_0^h \frac{\partial v}{\partial y}\,dy = -\int_0^h \frac{\partial u}{\partial x}\,dy. \tag{2.10}$$

Integrating Equation (2.9) with respect to y, where the upper limit h is outside the boundary layer (with $h \gg \delta$), we have

Often $h = \infty$ is taken.

$$\int_0^h \left(u\frac{\partial u}{\partial x} + v\frac{\partial u}{\partial y} - U\frac{dU}{dx}\right)dy = \int_0^h \nu\frac{\partial^2 u}{\partial y^2}\,dy. \tag{2.11}$$

Now, using integration by parts, the continuity equation (2.1) and Equation (2.10), we have

$$\int_0^h v\frac{\partial u}{\partial y}\,dy = [uv]_0^h - \int_0^h u\frac{\partial v}{\partial y}\,dy$$

$$= U\,v(x,h) + \int_0^h u\frac{\partial u}{\partial x}\,dy$$

$$= \int_0^h \left(u\frac{\partial u}{\partial x} - U\frac{\partial u}{\partial x}\right)dy.$$

Also the right-hand side of Equation (2.11) is

$$\int_0^h \nu \frac{\partial^2 u}{\partial y^2} \, dy = \left[\nu \frac{\partial u}{\partial y} \right]_0^h = -\left[\nu \frac{\partial u}{\partial y} \right]_{y=0}.$$

Hence Equation (2.11) becomes

$$\int_0^h \left(2u \frac{\partial u}{\partial x} - U \frac{\partial u}{\partial x} - U \frac{dU}{dx} \right) dy = -\left[\nu \frac{\partial u}{\partial y} \right]_{y=0}. \qquad (2.12)$$

The first two terms in the integrand on the left-hand side can be expressed respectively as

$$2u \frac{\partial u}{\partial x} = \frac{\partial(u^2)}{\partial x} \qquad \text{and} \qquad -U \frac{\partial u}{\partial x} = -\frac{\partial(uU)}{\partial x} + u \frac{dU}{dx},$$

and so Equation (2.12) becomes

$$\int_0^h \left[\frac{\partial}{\partial x} (u^2 - uU) + (u - U) \frac{dU}{dx} \right] dy = -\left[\nu \frac{\partial u}{\partial y} \right]_{y=0}.$$

After further manipulation and a sign change, we obtain

$$\frac{d}{dx} \left(U^2 \int_0^h \frac{u}{U} \left(1 - \frac{u}{U} \right) dy \right) + U \frac{dU}{dx} \int_0^h \left(1 - \frac{u}{U} \right) dy = \left[\nu \frac{\partial u}{\partial y} \right]_{y=0}.$$

Defining

$$\delta_1(x) = \int_0^h \left(1 - \frac{u}{U} \right) dy \qquad \text{and} \qquad \delta_2(x) = \int_0^h \frac{u}{U} \left(1 - \frac{u}{U} \right) dy,$$

we have

$$\frac{d}{dx} (U^2 \delta_2) + U \frac{dU}{dx} \delta_1 = \left[\nu \frac{\partial u}{\partial y} \right]_{y=0};$$

that is,

$$\frac{d\delta_2}{dx} + (\delta_1 + 2\delta_2) \frac{1}{U} \frac{dU}{dx} = \frac{\nu}{U^2} \left[\frac{\partial u}{\partial y} \right]_{y=0}.$$

Finally, writing

$$\tau_0 = \left[\mu \frac{\partial u}{\partial y} \right]_{y=0} = \nu\rho \left[\frac{\partial u}{\partial y} \right]_{y=0}$$

for the shear stress at the surface, we obtain the **momentum integral equation**

$$\frac{d\delta_2}{dx} + (\delta_1 + 2\delta_2) \frac{1}{U} \frac{dU}{dx} = \frac{\tau_0}{\rho U^2}. \qquad (2.13)$$

The right-hand side here is half the skin friction coefficient, c_f.

The quantities δ_1 and δ_2 have a physical interpretation. Unlike δ, they each give a definite measure of 'effective boundary layer thickness'. Thus

$$\delta_1(x) = \int_0^h \left(1 - \frac{u}{U} \right) dy \qquad (2.14)$$

is the **displacement thickness** of the boundary layer. It is the distance by which the solid boundary should be displaced in the y-direction to give the same mean flow rate as for inviscid flow without the boundary layer. This is illustrated geometrically in Figure 2.3.

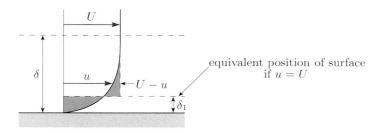

Figure 2.3

Since

$$U\delta_1 = \int_0^h (U - u)\, dy,$$

the two shaded areas are equal.

The quantity

$$\delta_2(x) = \int_0^h \frac{u}{U} \left(1 - \frac{u}{U}\right) dy \tag{2.15}$$

In some texts, δ_1 and δ_2 are denoted by δ^* and θ, respectively.

is known as the **momentum thickness**. It is the thickness of a layer of the external stream that carries a momentum flow rate equal to the reduction caused by the presence of the boundary layer.

Given a velocity profile $u(x,y)$, the displacement thickness $\delta_1(x)$ (from Equation (2.14)) and the momentum thickness $\delta_2(x)$ (from Equation (2.15)) can be calculated. If the velocity profile is given in the dimensionless form

$$\frac{u}{U} = f\left(\frac{y}{\delta}\right) \qquad \left(0 \le \frac{y}{\delta} \le 1\right),$$

where δ is an assumed outer limit for the boundary layer, then each of δ_1 and δ_2 is found to be a multiple of δ. Also τ_0 can be found in terms of δ. Then the momentum integral equation (2.13) becomes a differential equation to be solved for δ, following which each of δ and τ_0 can be expressed in terms of x, and the drag on the surface due to the flow past it can be found. This is best illustrated by means of an example.

The cases to be considered now are all for flow past a flat plate with zero pressure gradient, $dp/dx = 0$. From Equation (2.8) it follows that $dU/dx = 0$; so the momentum integral equation reduces to

$$\frac{d\delta_2}{dx} = \frac{\tau_0}{\rho U^2}. \tag{2.16}$$

Example 2.1

Consider the trial velocity profile

$$\frac{u}{U} = f\left(\frac{y}{\delta}\right) = 2\left(\frac{y}{\delta}\right) - \left(\frac{y}{\delta}\right)^2 \qquad \left(0 \le \frac{y}{\delta} \le 1\right)$$

for a boundary layer flow with zero external pressure gradient.

(a) Show that this profile satisfies certain boundary conditions of the problem but not others.

(b) What is the corresponding shear stress distribution across the boundary layer? Show that the given profile does not satisfy the result of Exercise 2.1(b).

(c) Find the displacement thickness δ_1 and momentum thickness δ_2 in terms of δ, and hence obtain a differential equation for δ.

(d) By solving this equation, express δ and τ_0 in terms of x. Calculate the corresponding total skin friction drag (per unit breadth perpendicular to the flow) on a plate of length L.

It is assumed that $u/U = 1$ for $y/\delta > 1$.

A graph of the trial profile is shown in Figure 2.4.

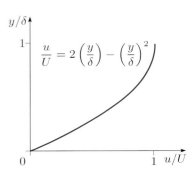

Figure 2.4

75

Solution

(a) The necessary boundary conditions were discussed at the end of Subsection 2.1. The trial velocity profile

$$\frac{u}{U} = f\left(\frac{y}{\delta}\right) = 2\left(\frac{y}{\delta}\right) - \left(\frac{y}{\delta}\right)^2 \qquad \left(0 \le \frac{y}{\delta} \le 1\right)$$

satisfies the boundary conditions

$$u = 0 \text{ at } y = 0, \qquad u = U \text{ and } \frac{\partial u}{\partial y} = 0 \text{ at } y = \delta.$$

However, $\partial^2 u/\partial y^2 \ne 0$ at $y = \delta$.

(b) The shear stress in the boundary layer is given by $\tau = \mu\,\partial u/\partial y$; so here

$$\tau = \frac{2\mu U}{\delta}\left(1 - \frac{y}{\delta}\right),$$

which varies linearly with y across the boundary layer. At the plate $(y = 0)$, we have

$$\tau_0 = \frac{2\mu U}{\delta},$$

which will be of use in part (c) below. Also

$$\frac{\partial \tau}{\partial y} = -\frac{2\mu U}{\delta^2},$$

and since $dU/dx = 0$ (from Equation (2.8)), the given profile does not satisfy the result of Exercise 2.1(b).

(The result of Exercise 2.1(b) appears to give another boundary condition that should be satisfied by u, namely,

$$\frac{\partial^2 u}{\partial y^2} = -\frac{U}{\nu}\frac{dU}{dx} \quad \text{at } y = 0.$$

In the case of zero external pressure gradient, this becomes

$$\frac{\partial^2 u}{\partial y^2} = 0 \quad \text{at } y = 0.$$

The mismatches between the trial velocity profile for u and the values of $\partial^2 u/\partial y^2$ at $y = 0$ and $y = \delta$ are a symptom of the fact that u does not exactly satisfy the boundary layer equations, and in particular does not satisfy them at either end of the interval $[0, \delta]$.)

(c) The integrals for δ_1 and δ_2 can be simplified by setting the upper limit at δ (since $u/U = 1$ for $y/\delta > 1$) and noting that, from integration by substitution,

$$\int_0^\delta g\left(\frac{y}{\delta}\right) dy = \delta \int_0^1 g(\eta)\,d\eta, \qquad \text{where } \eta = \frac{y}{\delta}.$$

Hence from Equation (2.14),

$$\frac{\delta_1}{\delta} = \int_0^1 \left(1 - \frac{u}{U}\right) d\eta = \int_0^1 \left(1 - 2\eta + \eta^2\right) d\eta$$
$$= \left[\eta - \eta^2 + \tfrac{1}{3}\eta^3\right]_0^1 = \tfrac{1}{3},$$

so that $\delta_1 = \tfrac{1}{3}\delta$.

Despite its shortcomings, this 'trial profile' can still be used to obtain expressions for $\delta(x)$ and $\tau_0(x)$. It has been chosen as a simple function which looks somewhat like the observed profile. (For pipe flow, this function gives an exact solution, but the circumstances of pipe flow differ from those of external flow past a plate.)

Similarly, from Equation (2.15),

$$\frac{\delta_2}{\delta} = \int_0^1 \frac{u}{U}\left(1 - \frac{u}{U}\right) d\eta = \int_0^1 \left(2\eta - \eta^2\right)\left(1 - 2\eta + \eta^2\right) d\eta$$

$$= \int_0^1 \left(2\eta - 5\eta^2 + 4\eta^3 - \eta^4\right) d\eta$$

$$= \left[\eta^2 - \tfrac{5}{3}\eta^3 + \eta^4 - \tfrac{1}{5}\eta^5\right]_0^1 = \tfrac{2}{15},$$

so that $\delta_2 = \frac{2}{15}\delta$. From part (b), we also have $\tau_0 = 2\mu U/\delta$. Hence the momentum integral equation (2.16) becomes

$$\frac{2}{15}\frac{d\delta}{dx} = \frac{2\mu U}{\rho U^2 \delta}, \qquad \text{or} \qquad \frac{d(\delta^2)}{dx} = \frac{30\nu}{U}.$$

(d) On integrating, we have

$$\delta^2 = \frac{30\nu}{U}x \qquad (\text{since } \delta = 0 \text{ when } x = 0) \qquad \text{or}$$

$$\delta = 5.477 \left(\frac{\nu x}{U}\right)^{1/2}.$$

This can also be written in dimensionless form as

$$\frac{\delta}{x} = 5.477(Re_x)^{-1/2}, \qquad \text{where } Re_x = \frac{Ux}{\nu}.$$

From $\tau_0 = 2\mu U/\delta$, we also have

$$\tau_0 = \frac{2\mu U}{\sqrt{30}}\left(\frac{U}{\nu x}\right)^{1/2} = 0.365\left(\frac{\mu\rho U^3}{x}\right)^{1/2}.$$

Equivalently, the (dimensionless) skin friction coefficient is

$$c_f = \frac{\tau_0}{\frac{1}{2}\rho U^2} = 0.730(Re_x)^{-1/2}.$$

The total skin friction drag per unit breadth on (one side of) a plate of length L is

$$F_L = \int_0^L \tau_0\, dx = \left[0.730(\mu\rho U^3 x)^{1/2}\right]_0^L$$

$$= 0.730(\mu\rho U^3 L)^{1/2}. \quad \blacksquare$$

Several features of the solution to Example 2.1 generalise to other trial velocity profiles. In each case, dimensionless numbers K_1, K_2, K_3 and K_4 can be found for which

$$\left.\begin{array}{l}
\dfrac{\delta}{x} = K_1(Re_x)^{-1/2}, \qquad \dfrac{\delta_1}{\delta} = K_3, \qquad \dfrac{\delta_1}{\delta_2} = K_4, \\[2mm]
c_f = \dfrac{\tau_0}{\frac{1}{2}\rho U^2} = K_2(Re_x)^{-1/2} \text{ and } F_L = K_2(\mu\rho U^3 L)^{1/2}.
\end{array}\right\} \quad (2.17)$$

For Example 2.1, we have

$$K_1 = 5.477, \quad K_2 = 0.730, \quad K_3 = 0.333, \quad K_4 = 2.50.$$

Exercise 2.2

Consider the trial velocity profile

$$\frac{u}{U} = \frac{y}{\delta} \qquad \left(0 \le \frac{y}{\delta} \le 1\right).$$

Find the displacement thickness δ_1 and momentum thickness δ_2, assuming that the external pressure gradient dp/dx is zero. Hence find the boundary layer thickness δ and shear stress τ_0 at the plate in terms of x, and calculate the total skin friction drag (per unit breadth perpendicular to the flow) on a plate of length L. State the values of the constants K_1, K_2, K_3 and K_4 in Equations (2.17).

As elsewhere, the total skin friction drag on one side of the plate is sought.

The procedure of Example 2.1 and Exercise 2.2 represents what might be tried if there were no other approach to solving the problem. The trial profiles are selected because they match certain of the boundary conditions of the problem and have 'roughly the right shape', as compared with observations. By specifying $u/U = f(y/\delta)$, where $\delta(x)$ is an assumed finite thickness for the boundary layer, the momentum integral equation leads to estimates of the boundary layer thickness, shear stress at the surface, and total skin friction drag on the plate.

Relatively simple trial profiles have a part to play if the accuracy of the estimates provided can be assessed, but as yet we have little means for doing this. It might be expected that the linear velocity profile in Exercise 2.2 gives worse estimates than the parabolic profile in Example 2.1, since it fails to satisfy the condition $\partial u/\partial y = 0$ at $y = \delta$ (and correspondingly the shear stress $\tau = \mu\,\partial u/\partial y$ has a discontinuity at $y = \delta$, being constant across the boundary layer but zero outside it). The parabolic profile satisfies this boundary condition, as well as $u = 0$ at $y = 0$ and $u = U$ at $y = \delta$.

In fact, an exact solution of the boundary layer equations can be found when the external pressure gradient is zero, as you will see in the next subsection. This permits an appraisal of how good the earlier estimates are. However, the work so far has been of considerable assistance to the solution process by showing that, if one assumes a solution of the form

$$\frac{u}{U} = f\left(\frac{y}{\delta}\right), \qquad \text{where } \delta = \delta(x),$$

then $\delta(x) \propto (\nu x/U)^{1/2}$. This indicates that the boundary layer over a flat plate, with zero external pressure gradient, grows at a rate proportional to $x^{1/2}$, as indicated in Figure 2.5. The same applies to the displacement thickness δ_1 and the momentum thickness δ_2, since these were found to be multiples of δ.

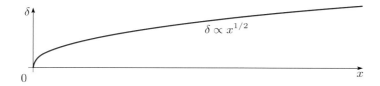

Figure 2.5

It is to be expected that better estimates of boundary layer flow parameters will be found by using trial velocity profiles that fit more of the boundary conditions, and taking higher-degree polynomial functions will enable this to be done. You are asked to consider the case of a cubic function in Exercise 2.9. The quartic trial profile

$$\frac{u}{U} = f\left(\frac{y}{\delta}\right) = 2\left(\frac{y}{\delta}\right) - 2\left(\frac{y}{\delta}\right)^3 + \left(\frac{y}{\delta}\right)^4 \tag{2.18}$$

satisfies all of the boundary conditions

$$\left.\begin{array}{l} u(x,0) = \dfrac{\partial^2 u}{\partial y^2}(x,0) = 0, \\[3mm] u(x,\delta) - U = \dfrac{\partial u}{\partial y}(x,\delta) = \dfrac{\partial^2 u}{\partial y^2}(x,\delta) = 0. \end{array}\right\} \tag{2.19}$$

For this function, the parameters defined in Equations (2.17) have the values

$$K_1 = 5.840, \quad K_2 = 0.686, \quad K_3 = 0.300, \quad K_4 = 2.55.$$

Exercise 2.3

Verify that the trial velocity profile given by Equation (2.18) satisfies the five boundary conditions (2.19).

2.3   Solutions to the boundary layer equations

In this subsection we indicate how an exact solution may be found to the boundary layer equations

$$\frac{\partial u}{\partial x} + \frac{\partial v}{\partial y} = 0, \tag{2.1}$$

$$u\frac{\partial u}{\partial x} + v\frac{\partial u}{\partial y} = U\frac{dU}{dx} + \nu\frac{\partial^2 u}{\partial y^2}, \tag{2.9}$$

when the external pressure gradient dp/dx is zero. In this case we have $dU/dx = 0$, from Equation (2.8), and so Equation (2.9) reduces to

$$u\frac{\partial u}{\partial x} + v\frac{\partial u}{\partial y} = \nu\frac{\partial^2 u}{\partial y^2}. \tag{2.20}$$

An exact solution to the boundary layer equations was first found by Paul Richard Heinrich Blasius in 1908. It is however only an approximate solution to the Navier–Stokes equations, since these are approximated by one of the boundary layer equations.

The work in Subsection 2.2 indicates that it may be profitable to work with the dimensionless parameter

$$\eta = \frac{y}{(\nu x/U)^{1/2}}, \tag{2.21}$$

since in each case the assumed finite thickness of the boundary layer δ was found to be proportional to $(\nu x/U)^{1/2}$. To deal with the continuity equation (2.1) we use the stream function $\psi(x,y)$, for which

$$u = \frac{\partial \psi}{\partial y}, \qquad v = -\frac{\partial \psi}{\partial x}. \tag{2.22}$$

The stream function was introduced in *Unit 5* Section 2.

Then Equation (2.1) is automatically satisfied.

On putting

$$\psi(x, y) = (Ux\nu)^{1/2} f(\eta),$$

where η is given by Equation (2.21), we obtain the following from Equations (2.22):

$$u = \frac{\partial \psi}{\partial y} = (Ux\nu)^{1/2}(\nu x/U)^{-1/2} f'(\eta) = U f'(\eta), \qquad (2.23)$$

Note that $\psi/(Ux\nu)^{1/2}$ is dimensionless, and that f here has no connection with the trial velocity profiles in Subsection 2.2.

There is no need to follow the detailed manipulations here, to obtain Equation (2.26).

$$v = -\frac{\partial \psi}{\partial x} = -\tfrac{1}{2}(U\nu/x)^{1/2} f(\eta) - (Ux\nu)^{1/2}(-\tfrac{1}{2})y(\nu x^3/U)^{-1/2} f'(\eta)$$

$$= \tfrac{1}{2}(U\nu/x)^{1/2} \left[-f(\eta) + \eta f'(\eta) \right]. \qquad (2.24)$$

On taking further derivatives, we have

$$\left.\begin{array}{ll} \dfrac{\partial u}{\partial x} = -\dfrac{Uy}{2(\nu x^3/U)^{1/2}} f''(\eta) = -\dfrac{U}{2x} \eta f''(\eta), \\[4mm] \dfrac{\partial u}{\partial y} = \dfrac{U}{(\nu x/U)^{1/2}} f''(\eta), \qquad \dfrac{\partial^2 u}{\partial y^2} = \dfrac{U}{\nu x/U} f'''(\eta). \end{array}\right\} \qquad (2.25)$$

Substituting into the boundary layer equation (2.20) gives the third-order ordinary differential equation

$$2f'''(\eta) + f(\eta)f''(\eta) = 0, \qquad (2.26)$$

which is known as the *Blasius equation*. While Equation (2.26) is non-linear and cannot be solved analytically, a numerical solution is straightforward. However, boundary conditions on the function f are needed for this purpose. Since $u = v = 0$ at $y = 0$, Equations (2.23) and (2.24) give $f'(0) = f(0) = 0$. Also, since $u \to U$ as $y \to \infty$, Equation (2.23) gives $f'(\eta) \to 1$ as $\eta \to \infty$. The conditions

$$f(0) = f'(0) = 0 \quad \text{and} \quad \lim_{\eta \to \infty} f'(\eta) = 1$$

suffice for a unique solution of the Blasius equation (2.26) to be found, and corresponding tabulated values are shown in Table 2.1. Note that

$$f'(\eta) = \frac{u}{U},$$

from Equation (2.23), while

$$\frac{f''(\eta)}{f''(0)} = \frac{\partial u/\partial y}{[\partial u/\partial y]_{y=0}} = \frac{\tau}{\tau_0},$$

from the second of Equations (2.25). Hence a graph of η against $f'(\eta)$ shows the velocity profile across the boundary layer, for any x, while a plot of η against $f''(\eta)/f''(0)$ similarly shows the shear stress profile. These graphs are shown in Figure 2.6, below Table 2.1.

Table 2.1   Numerical solution to the Blasius equation

$\eta \left(= \dfrac{y}{(\nu x/U)^{1/2}} \right)$	$f(\eta)$	$f'(\eta) \left(= \dfrac{u}{U} \right)$	$f''(\eta)$	$\dfrac{f''(\eta)}{f''(0)} \left(= \dfrac{\tau}{\tau_0} \right)$
0	0	0	0.33206	1.0000
0.2	0.00664	0.06641	0.33199	0.9998
0.4	0.02656	0.13277	0.33147	0.9982
1.0	0.16557	0.32979	0.32301	0.9727
1.4	0.32298	0.45627	0.30787	0.9272
2.0	0.65003	0.62977	0.26675	0.8033
2.4	0.92230	0.72899	0.22809	0.6869
3.0	1.39682	0.84605	0.16136	0.4859
3.4	1.74696	0.90177	0.11788	0.3550
4.0	2.30576	0.95552	0.06424	0.1935
4.4	2.69238	0.97587	0.03897	0.1174
5.0	3.28329	0.99155	0.01591	0.0479
5.4	3.68094	0.99616	0.00793	0.0239
6.0	4.27964	0.99898	0.00240	0.0072
7.0	5.27926	0.99992	0.00022	0.0007

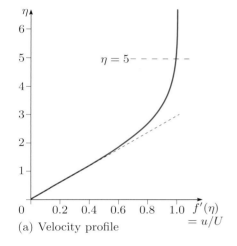

(a) Velocity profile

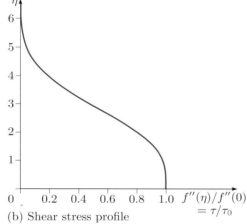

(b) Shear stress profile

Figure 2.6

Traditionally, the edge of a boundary layer has been defined as the point at which the velocity is within 1% of the free stream value outside the boundary layer (i.e. where $u/U = 0.99$). It is clear from Table 2.1 that $f'(\eta) = 0.99$ when $\eta = 5.0$, thus defining the thickness of a laminar boundary layer. However, if the criterion of shear stress is used instead, and the limit is defined in terms of the point at which the local shear stress is just 1% of the boundary shear stress, τ_0, then the values in the last column of Table 2.1 indicate that the edge of the boundary layer would be at $\eta = 6.0$, some 20% thicker than obtained by basing it on velocity. If the 99% rule for u/U is adopted, as is usual practice, this leads to $\tau/\tau_0 \simeq 5\%$ at the edge of this laminar boundary layer.

As Table 2.1 and Figure 2.6 both illustrate, the velocity increases almost linearly very close to the boundary, with $\partial u/\partial y \propto f''(\eta) \simeq 0.332$. Correspondingly, the shear stress in this region close to the boundary is almost constant (for fixed x).

Both $\partial u/\partial y$ and τ vary with x, however.

Taking $y = \delta$ when $\eta = y/(\nu x/U)^{1/2} = 5$, as above, gives

$$\delta = 5\left(\frac{\nu x}{U}\right)^{1/2} \quad \text{or} \quad \frac{\delta}{x} = 5(Re_x)^{-1/2}, \quad \text{where } Re_x = \frac{Ux}{\nu}.$$

Comparing with Equations (2.17), we have $K_1 = 5$ for this exact solution. Also, from the second of Equations (2.25) and Table 2.1, we obtain

$$c_f = \frac{\tau_0}{\frac{1}{2}\rho U^2} = \frac{1}{\frac{1}{2}\rho U^2}\left[\mu\frac{\partial u}{\partial y}\right]_{y=0} = \frac{\mu U}{\frac{1}{2}\rho U^2(\nu x/U)^{1/2}}f''(0)$$

$$= 0.664\left(\frac{\nu}{Ux}\right)^{1/2} = 0.664(Re_x)^{-1/2},$$

so that $K_2 = 0.664$. The displacement thickness is

$$\delta_1 = \int_0^\infty \left(1 - \frac{u}{U}\right) dy.$$

In terms of $\eta = y/(\nu x/U)^{1/2}$, we have

$$\left(\frac{\nu x}{U}\right)^{-1/2}\delta_1 = \int_0^\infty \left(1 - f'(\eta)\right) d\eta$$

$$= \lim_{\eta \to \infty} \left[\eta - f(\eta)\right] = 1.721,$$

so that $\delta_1 = 1.721(\nu x/U)^{1/2}$ and $K_3 = 1.721/5 = 0.344$. The momentum thickness is given, using integration by parts, by

$$\left(\frac{\nu x}{U}\right)^{-1/2}\delta_2 = \int_0^\infty f'(\eta)\left(1 - f'(\eta)\right) d\eta$$

$$= \left[f(\eta)\left(1 - f'(\eta)\right)\right]_0^\infty + \int_0^\infty f(\eta)f''(\eta)\, d\eta.$$

The first term is zero, since $f(0) = 0$ and $f'(\eta) \to 1$ as $\eta \to \infty$. The remaining integrand is equal to $-2f'''(\eta)$, from the Blasius equation (2.26). Hence

$$\left(\frac{\nu x}{U}\right)^{-1/2}\delta_2 = -2\int_0^\infty f'''(\eta)\, d\eta$$

$$= -2\left[f''(\eta)\right]_0^\infty = 2f''(0) = 0.664,$$

so that $\delta_2 = 0.664(\nu x/U)^{1/2}$ and $K_4 = 1.721/0.664 = 2.59$.

The following table shows how the exact values for the parameters K_1 to K_4, just found, compare with the estimated values corresponding to various trial velocity profiles.

> There is no need to follow the detailed calculations here to obtain K_1 to K_4 for the solution to the Blasius equation. The bottom row of Table 2.2 shows these values.

> Here we take $h = \infty$ in Equation (2.14), and similarly below in Equation (2.15).

> The limiting value 1.721 is already apparent at $\eta = 7$ from the last line of Table 2.1.

Table 2.2   Comparison of parameter values

Form for $\dfrac{u}{U}$	$K_1 = \dfrac{\delta}{x}(Re_x)^{1/2}$	$K_2 = c_f(Re_x)^{1/2}$	$K_3 = \dfrac{\delta_1}{\delta}$	$K_4 = \dfrac{\delta_1}{\delta_2}$
$\dfrac{y}{\delta}$	3.464	0.577	0.500	3.00
$2\left(\dfrac{y}{\delta}\right) - \left(\dfrac{y}{\delta}\right)^2$	5.477	0.730	0.333	2.50
$\dfrac{3}{2}\left(\dfrac{y}{\delta}\right) - \dfrac{1}{2}\left(\dfrac{y}{\delta}\right)^3$	4.640	0.646	0.375	2.69
$2\left(\dfrac{y}{\delta}\right) - 2\left(\dfrac{y}{\delta}\right)^3 + \left(\dfrac{y}{\delta}\right)^4$	5.840	0.686	0.300	2.55
$\sin\left(\dfrac{\pi y}{2\delta}\right)$	4.795	0.655	0.363	2.66
exact solution	5.000	0.664	0.344	2.59

Apart from the linear profile, each of the trial functions gives estimates which are reasonably close to those of the exact solution, and similarly, the graphs of these functions look quite close to that of the exact solution, as shown in Figure 2.7.

The graph of the quartic trial profile is not included in Figure 2.7.

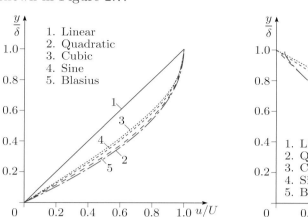

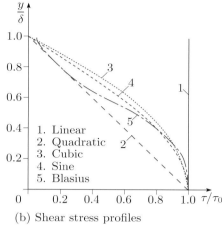

(a) Velocity profiles   (b) Shear stress profiles

Figure 2.7

Exercise 2.4

A smooth rectangular flat plate, with sides of length p and $4p$, is held parallel to a uniform stream. Assuming that flow in the boundary layer is laminar throughout, state whether the total skin friction drag is greater when the shorter side is held parallel to the direction of flow or when the longer side is parallel to the flow.

After seeking a qualitative answer by physical reasoning, calculate the ratio of the two drag forces. If it is necessary to apply a particular model, then use the exact solution to the Blasius equation.

Exercise 2.5

Water from a uniform stream, with speed $U = 1\,\mathrm{m\,s^{-1}}$, flows past a plate of length 30 cm held parallel to the flow. Use the exact solution of the Blasius equation to calculate the total skin friction drag per unit breadth exerted by the stream on one side of the plate.

For water, take $\mu = 1.0 \times 10^{-3}\,\mathrm{kg\,m^{-1}\,s^{-1}}$ and $\rho = 1.0 \times 10^{3}\,\mathrm{kg\,m^{-3}}$.

The Blasius equation corresponds to the case in which there is zero external presure gradient, so that $dU/dx = 0$. In a similar manner, it can be shown that if $U \propto x^m$ (corresponding to a non-zero external pressure gradient), and if the stream function is taken as

There will be no assessment of the rest of this subsection.

$$\psi(x,y) = \left(\frac{Ux\nu}{m+1}\right)^{1/2} f(\eta), \qquad \text{where } \eta = y\left(\frac{\nu x}{(m+1)U}\right)^{-1/2},$$

Note for these expressions that U is now a function of x.

then $f(\eta)$ satisfies the equation

$$2f'''(\eta) + f(\eta)f''(\eta) + \beta\left(1 - \left(f'(\eta)\right)^2\right) = 0, \qquad \text{where } \beta = \frac{2m}{m+1}.$$

This is known as the *Falkner–Skan equation*, and like the Blasius equation (2.26) (which is the special case for $m = 0$) it can be solved numerically with the same boundary conditions as before.

See the *Media Guide* for more on the derivation of the Blasius and Falkner–Skan equations.

It turns out that an external flow of the form $U \propto x^m$ corresponds geometrically to flow past a wedge of angle $\pi\beta$ (where $\beta = 2m/(m+1)$ as above), as shown in Figure 2.8 (overleaf).

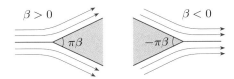

Figure 2.8

Some corresponding exact velocity profiles for various values of m are shown in Figure 2.9. Note that for negative values of m, the profile has a point of inflection. This is connected to the occurrence of boundary layer separation, as described in the next subsection.

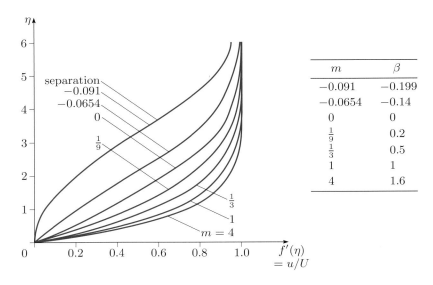

m	β
-0.091	-0.199
-0.0654	-0.14
0	0
$\frac{1}{9}$	0.2
$\frac{1}{3}$	0.5
1	1
4	1.6

Figure 2.9

2.4   Boundary layer separation

As explained in Subsection 2.1, the boundary layer equations and solutions to them can be applied to flow past a curved boundary surface, provided that the curvature of the surface is not too large.

There will be no assessment of this subsection.

Consider the flow in the inviscid region past a cylinder, as shown in Figure 2.10.

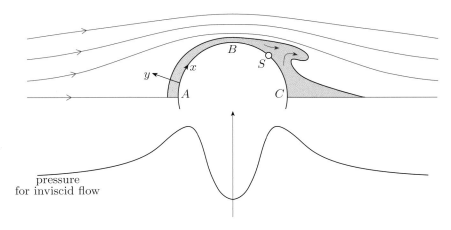

pressure
for inviscid flow

Figure 2.10

Owing to the presence of the cylinder, the streamlines become more tightly packed between point A and the midpoint B, and then space out again over the back half of the cylinder, from B to C. In other words, the external flow accelerates between A and B, but slows down between B and C. These changes in speed can only be due (in inviscid flow) to the pressure gradient, so there must be a pressure gradient $dp/dx < 0$ to accelerate fluid from A to B, and an adverse pressure gradient $dp/dx > 0$ to decelerate fluid from B to C. The inviscid flow is symmetric from front to back of the cylinder, with potential energy in the pressure field being converted to kinetic energy from A to B and then back to potential energy (without any loss) between B and C.

This is a consequence of Euler's equation or Bernoulli's equation; see Equation (2.8).

Recall here that x is the coordinate along the surface, while y is measured in the local normal direction.

Within the boundary layer, as was shown in Subsection 2.1, $\partial p/\partial y = 0$ and hence $p = p(x)$. So the variations of pressure in the inviscid (external) region must be replicated within the boundary layer.

The action of viscosity within the boundary layer causes a dissipation of energy. The fluid may not therefore have sufficient energy to reach C, so that its velocity becomes zero at some intervening point S, beyond which the velocity in close proximity to the surface is reversed and there is a curve leading away from the surface along which $u = 0$. In such a case, we call S the *separation point* for the flow.

This physical argument is confirmed by considering the boundary layer equation (2.7) at $y = 0$, where $u = v = 0$, which can be written as

$$\left[\frac{\partial^2 u}{\partial y^2}\right]_{y=0} = \frac{1}{\mu}\frac{dp}{dx}.$$

This says that at the cylinder's surface, $\partial^2 u/\partial y^2$ has the same sign as the pressure gradient, dp/dx. By contrast, the value of $\partial^2 u/\partial y^2$ towards the outside of the boundary layer must always be negative, because $\partial^2 u/\partial y^2 \to 0$ from below as the velocity profile matches smoothly onto the external flow.

At a position x along the surface at which $dp/dx < 0$, it follows that $\partial^2 u/\partial y^2 < 0$ for all y, so the velocity profile has the form shown in Figure 2.11(a). On the other hand, at a position x for which $dp/dx > 0$ (adverse pressure gradient), we have $\partial^2 u/\partial y^2 > 0$ at $y = 0$ and $\partial^2 u/\partial y^2 < 0$ towards the edge of the boundary layer; so at some y-value there must be a point of inflection in the graph of u, as indicated in Figure 2.11(b).

Roughly speaking, this is mirrored in the development of the graphs of Figure 2.9.

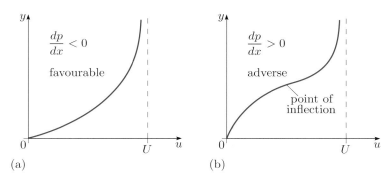

Figure 2.11

As dp/dx increases (moving along the surface in the direction of flow), so too does $\left[\partial^2 u/\partial y^2\right]_{y=0}$, causing increasing distortion of the velocity profile across the boundary layer. Eventually the value $\left[\partial u/\partial y\right]_{y=0} = 0$ may occur, which defines the separation point, S.

The development of the velocity profile in the direction of an increasing adverse pressure gradient is indicated in Figure 2.12. Beyond S we have $[\partial u/\partial y]_{y=0} < 0$ and hence negative values of u close to the surface. The corresponding pattern of flow is as shown in Figure 2.13.

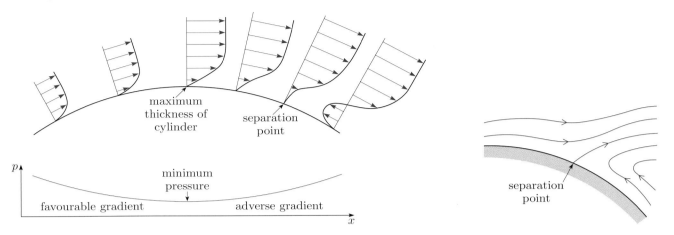

Figure 2.12   Figure 2.13

Beyond the separation point S the boundary layer becomes much thicker, and the boundary layer equations as developed earlier no longer apply. The flow beyond S is that of a wake filled with vortices. This region exerts a profile drag on the cylinder that is much larger than the viscous drag exerted at the surface. Consequently, for a body of non-streamlined shape where separation occurs, the profile drag is far greater than the skin friction drag.

This highlights the importance of streamlining in order to avoid or delay the onset of separation. It may even be preferable to induce the laminar flow to become turbulent, with greater skin friction drag, because boundary layer separation for turbulent flows occurs further along the body than for laminar flows, and hence the profile drag is reduced.

The dimples on golf balls achieve this purpose. The seam on a cricket ball can be used similarly, to affect the motion of the ball through the air.

2.5   Internal laminar flows

This section has so far considered laminar flows external to a solid surface. A challenging feature here was that the effective thickness of the boundary layer was always increasing (though more and more slowly), so that the flow never reached a fully developed state. This subsection, by contrast, looks at internal flows, for which it is very reasonable to assume that the flow has become fully developed. Much of this is revision of what was done in *Unit 8*. It is included here as a precursor to the consideration of turbulent internal flows in Section 4.

Consider a steady, uniform flow, with speed U, entering a cylindrical pipe as shown in cross-section in Figure 2.14. Owing to the drag exerted at the pipe wall, an annular boundary layer will develop in a manner similar to that considered earlier for flow past a flat plate. However, eventually the thickness of this boundary layer will grow to the point where there is no longer any external flow, and the flow is then 'all boundary layer'. Subsequently, the flow may be considered as fully developed, with no velocity changes in the direction of flow. The length of pipe prior to the disappearance of the external flow is called the *development length*.

This description applies to both laminar and turbulent flows, and both are illustrated in Figure 2.14. The development length is shorter in the turbulent case, because the turbulent boundary layer grows faster.

The development length is marked as l in Figure 2.14.

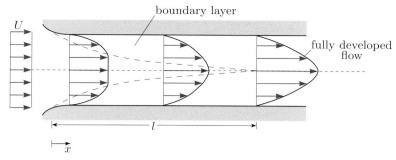

(a) Laminar flow ($Re < 2300$)

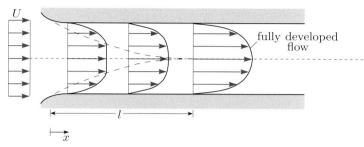

(b) Turbulent flow ($Re > 2300$)

Figure 2.14

Exercise 2.6

By applying Bernoulli's equation in the entry section of the pipe external to the boundary layer, together with the constancy of the volume flow rate, show that the pressure falls along the axis of the pipe throughout the development length.

Once the flow is fully developed, the pressure gradient is constant along the pipe, say $dp/dx = -C$, where $C > 0$ and x measures distance along the pipe. The Navier–Stokes equations for this flow reduce to

$$\frac{\mu}{r} \frac{d}{dr} \left(r \frac{du}{dr} \right) + C = 0, \tag{2.27}$$

See Equation (2.12) of *Unit 8*. Here x, u, $\mathbf{i}$ take the places of z, u_z, $\mathbf{k}$, respectively.

where $\mathbf{u}(r, \theta, z) = u(r)\,\mathbf{i}$. Taking a as the radius of the cylinder, the solution of Equation (2.27) that satisfies the no-slip boundary condition $u(a) = 0$ is

$$u(r) = \frac{C}{4\mu} \left(a^2 - r^2 \right),$$

See Equation (2.13) of *Unit 8*.

which has the parabolic profile suggested in Figure 2.14(a). The volume flow rate is

$$Q = \frac{\pi C a^4}{8\mu},$$

and the mean speed of flow is

$$U = \frac{C a^2}{8\mu} = \tfrac{1}{2} u(0).$$

This is the Hagen–Poiseuille equation. See Equation (2.14) of *Unit 8*.

Hence the mean speed of flow is half of the flow speed along the axis, which is the maximum speed.

The shear stress is, as before, $\tau = \mu\, \partial u / \partial y$, with y measured outwards from the pipe wall. Since $r = a - y$, this becomes

$$\tau(r) = -\mu \frac{\partial u}{\partial r}.$$

Exercise 2.7

How does the shear stress vary across the pipe? What is its value τ_0 at the pipe wall?

The results for the shear stress found in Exercise 2.7 can be shown to apply even without expressing the shear stress as $\tau = -\mu\,\partial u/\partial r$. Consider a length of pipe between positions x and $x + \delta x$, as shown in Figure 2.15. Since the flow is steady and fully developed, the forces acting on the water in this portion of pipe, considered as a block of fluid, must balance. The net force due to the pressure acting on the ends is

$$\pi a^2 [p(x) - p(x + \delta x)]\,\mathbf{i},$$

while the net force due to the shear stress acting around the surface of the curved wall is $-2\pi a\,\delta x\,\tau_0\,\mathbf{i}$. The sum of these two expressions should be zero. Dividing by δx and taking the limit as $\delta x \to 0$ gives

$$\tau_0 = -\tfrac{1}{2}a\frac{dp}{dx}. \tag{2.28}$$

In fact, the same argument can be applied to a cylindrical surface at any distance r from the axis of the pipe, so that

$$\tau(r) = -\tfrac{1}{2}r\frac{dp}{dx}.$$

A linear shear stress distribution can similarly be deduced for flow in an open channel. Figure 2.16 illustrates these results.

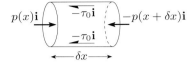

Figure 2.15   The shear stress shown at the pipe wall acts on the block of fluid, due to the wall. (There is an opposite stress on the wall, due to the fluid motion.)

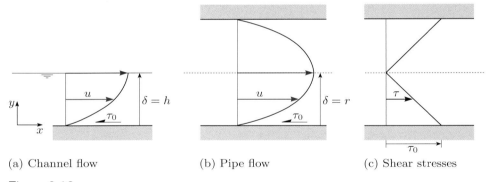

(a) Channel flow   (b) Pipe flow   (c) Shear stresses

Figure 2.16

This result of a linear shear stress distribution across the pipe from its centre has been derived *without* using the model for a Newtonian fluid, and indeed it applies also to turbulent (non-laminar) flow in a pipe.

Taking the *skin friction coefficient* for this situation to be

$$c_f = \frac{\tau_0}{\tfrac{1}{2}\rho U^2}, \qquad \text{where } U \text{ is the mean speed,} \tag{2.29}$$

Equation (2.28) gives

$$c_f = -\frac{a}{\rho U^2}\frac{dp}{dx} \qquad \text{or} \qquad \frac{dp}{dx} = -\frac{2\rho\,c_f}{d}U^2, \tag{2.30}$$

where d is the diameter of the pipe. This is a form of the *Darcy–Weisbach equation*, relating the pressure loss due to friction and the average speed of flow. It can also be written as

$$\Delta p = \frac{2\rho L c_f}{d}U^2,$$

where Δp is the pressure drop along a length L of pipe.

In the derivation of Equation (2.28), the factor $\frac{1}{2}a$ arose as a result of dividing the cross-sectional area $A = \pi a^2$ of the pipe by its perimeter, $P = 2\pi a$. The same argument can be applied to a pipe of non-circular cross-section, in which case $\frac{1}{2}a$ is replaced by the so-called *hydraulic radius*, $R = A/P$, where A is the cross-sectional area of the flow and P is the *wetted perimeter*. If the pipe is full, then P is its total perimeter, but if the pipe is not full then P is that portion of the perimeter which is below the liquid surface and hence 'wetted'. Equation (2.28) becomes

Note that, for a circular pipe, the hydraulic radius is only half of the actual radius.

$$\tau_m = -R\frac{dp}{dx},$$

where τ_m is the mean shear stress at the wall, and the Darcy–Weisbach equation becomes

$$\frac{dp}{dx} = -\frac{\rho\,c_f}{2R}U^2, \qquad \text{where } c_f = \frac{\tau_m}{\frac{1}{2}\rho U^2}.$$

In the case of laminar flow in a full circular pipe, where

$$U = \frac{Ca^2}{8\mu} = \frac{Cd^2}{32\mu} \qquad \text{and} \qquad \frac{dp}{dx} = -C,$$

Equation (2.30) gives

$$-C = -\frac{2\rho\,c_f U}{d} \times U = -\frac{2\rho\,c_f U}{d} \times \frac{Cd^2}{32\mu},$$

or

$$c_f = \frac{16\mu}{\rho dU} = \frac{16}{Re}, \qquad \text{where } Re = \frac{\rho dU}{\mu} = \frac{Ud}{\nu}. \tag{2.31}$$

For laminar flow in a full circular pipe, therefore, the skin friction coefficient given by Equation (2.29) is inversely proportional to the Reynolds number.

Formulas that involve c_f are often quoted in terms of the *Darcy friction factor*, $\lambda = 4c_f$. Hence Equation (2.31) is also quoted as $\lambda = 64/Re$.

Exercise 2.8

Figure 2.14(a) can also be regarded as depicting the steady laminar flow between infinite fixed parallel plates a distance h apart. Once the flow has become fully developed, the Navier–Stokes equations reduce to

This is known as *Poiseuille flow*.

$$\mu\frac{d^2u}{dy^2} + C = 0, \qquad \text{where } \frac{dp}{dx} = -C,$$

and $\mathbf{u}(x,y,z) = u(y)\,\mathbf{i}$. The solution satisfying the no-slip boundary conditions at $y = 0$ and $y = h$ is

See Equation (1.10) and Exercises 1.4 and 2.6 in *Unit 8*. Here y replaces z as the coordinate across the channel.

$$u(y) = \frac{Cy(h-y)}{2\mu}.$$

(a) Find an expression for the shear stress at the lower plate, τ_0, in terms of C, h and μ.

Similar results to those in this exercise also apply to flow in an open channel of depth $\frac{1}{2}h$.

(b) Find an expression for the mean flow speed, U.

(c) Hence find an expression for the skin friction coefficient

$$c_f = \frac{\tau_0}{\frac{1}{2}\rho U^2},$$

and show that $c_f \propto 1/Re$, where $Re = \rho U h/\mu$.

(d) What is the analogue of the Darcy–Weisbach equation (2.30) in this case?

End-of-section exercise

Consider the trial velocity profile

$$\frac{u}{U} = \frac{3}{2}\left(\frac{y}{\delta}\right) - \frac{1}{2}\left(\frac{y}{\delta}\right)^3 \qquad \left(0 \le \frac{y}{\delta} \le 1\right)$$

for the flow in a boundary layer past a flat plate with zero external pressure gradient.

(a) Which of the boundary conditions (2.19) does this function satisfy?

(b) Find the parameters K_1, K_2, K_3, K_4 of Equations (2.17) for this profile.

3   Modelling turbulent flow

This section introduces the most basic models for turbulent flow. In order for a proper interpretation to be made of the effects of turbulence on the mean flow velocity, it is necessary first to revisit the Navier–Stokes equations and see in greater detail how these are derived, which is done in Subsection 3.1. Then Subsection 3.2 shows how an 'averaged' version of the Navier–Stokes equations for turbulent flow can be obtained; this isolates the effects of turbulence in a way that makes the equations potentially more tractable. Subsection 3.3 shows how the momentum integral equation can be applied, as in Subsection 2.2 but now to turbulent flows. Then Subsection 3.4 explains how further turbulence models are needed to complete the picture described by the averaged Navier–Stokes equations in Subsection 3.2.

The discussion focuses on modelling the effects of turbulence on the mean flow, not on modelling the turbulence itself (which is beyond the scope of the course).

3.1   Reconstructing the Navier–Stokes equations

One special case of the Navier–Stokes equations was derived in *Unit 8* Subsection 1.3, following which the general equations were stated at the start of Subsection 2.1. We now explore in more detail how these equations arise.

The aim is to generalise Euler's equation,

$$\rho\frac{d\mathbf{u}}{dt} = -\boldsymbol{\nabla}p + \rho\mathbf{F}, \tag{3.1}$$

for the flow of an inviscid fluid, so that viscous effects are also taken into account. Hence we need to add to the pressure gradient, $-\boldsymbol{\nabla}p$, a term to represent viscous surface forces.

Consider the small rectangular block of fluid shown in Figure 3.1, with sides parallel to the Cartesian axes of lengths δx, δy and δz, respectively. The centre of the block has coordinates (x, y, z).

See Equations (2.2) of *Unit 8*.

The fluid is assumed to be incompressible throughout.

See *Unit 5* Subsection 5.1.

There will be no assessment of this subsection.

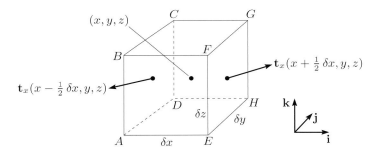

Figure 3.1

On each face of the block, the effect of all the surface forces acting can be represented by a *stress vector*. Suppose that the stress vectors acting on faces perpendicular to $\mathbf{i}$, $\mathbf{j}$ and $\mathbf{k}$ are denoted by $\mathbf{t}_x$, $\mathbf{t}_y$ and $\mathbf{t}_z$, respectively. Then the net force on the block due to the stresses on faces $ABCD$ and $EFGH$ (both perpendicular to $\mathbf{i}$) is

$$\left[\mathbf{t}_x(x + \tfrac{1}{2}\delta x, y, z) - \mathbf{t}_x(x - \tfrac{1}{2}\delta x, y, z)\right]\delta y\,\delta z \simeq \frac{\partial \mathbf{t}_x}{\partial x}\,\delta x\,\delta y\,\delta z.$$

Arguing similarly for the other two pairs of opposite faces, the net surface force on the block is approximately

$$\left(\frac{\partial \mathbf{t}_x}{\partial x} + \frac{\partial \mathbf{t}_y}{\partial y} + \frac{\partial \mathbf{t}_z}{\partial z}\right)\delta x\,\delta y\,\delta z,$$

so that the net surface force per unit volume is

$$\frac{\partial \mathbf{t}_x}{\partial x} + \frac{\partial \mathbf{t}_y}{\partial y} + \frac{\partial \mathbf{t}_z}{\partial z}. \tag{3.2}$$

This expression replaces $-\boldsymbol{\nabla}p$ (for the inviscid case) in Equation (3.1). Indeed, when there is no viscosity, we have

$$\mathbf{t}_x = -p\,\mathbf{i}, \qquad \mathbf{t}_y = -p\,\mathbf{j}, \qquad \mathbf{t}_z = -p\,\mathbf{k},$$

so that

$$\frac{\partial \mathbf{t}_x}{\partial x} + \frac{\partial \mathbf{t}_y}{\partial y} + \frac{\partial \mathbf{t}_z}{\partial z} = \frac{\partial}{\partial x}(-p\,\mathbf{i}) + \frac{\partial}{\partial y}(-p\,\mathbf{j}) + \frac{\partial}{\partial z}(-p\,\mathbf{k}) = -\boldsymbol{\nabla}p.$$

More generally, we express the three stress vectors as

$$\left.\begin{aligned}
\mathbf{t}_x &= (-p + \tau_{xx})\,\mathbf{i} + \tau_{xy}\,\mathbf{j} + \tau_{xz}\,\mathbf{k}, \\
\mathbf{t}_y &= \tau_{yx}\,\mathbf{i} + (-p + \tau_{yy})\,\mathbf{j} + \tau_{yz}\,\mathbf{k}, \\
\mathbf{t}_z &= \tau_{zx}\,\mathbf{i} + \tau_{zy}\,\mathbf{j} + (-p + \tau_{zz})\,\mathbf{k}.
\end{aligned}\right\} \tag{3.3}$$

Thus τ_{xy} is the component of the stress in the y-direction on a face perpendicular to $\mathbf{i}$, with a similar interpretation for other components. The value of p is chosen to be

$$p = -\tfrac{1}{3}\left(\mathbf{t}_x \cdot \mathbf{i} + \mathbf{t}_y \cdot \mathbf{j} + \mathbf{t}_z \cdot \mathbf{k}\right),$$

from which it follows that

$$\tau_{xx} + \tau_{yy} + \tau_{zz} = 0. \tag{3.4}$$

Furthermore, the matrix of components

$$\begin{pmatrix}
\tau_{xx} & \tau_{xy} & \tau_{xz} \\
\tau_{yx} & \tau_{yy} & \tau_{yz} \\
\tau_{zx} & \tau_{zy} & \tau_{zz}
\end{pmatrix} \tag{3.5}$$

must be *symmetric*, that is,

$$\tau_{yx} = \tau_{xy}, \qquad \tau_{zx} = \tau_{xz}, \qquad \tau_{zy} = \tau_{yz}. \tag{3.6}$$

The argument to show this is very similar to that given in *Unit 8* Subsection 1.3. These restrictions are necessary for the Torque Law to hold when applied to the block, in the limit as δx, δy, $\delta z \to 0$.

See Equations (1.9) and the following text in *Unit 8*.

On replacing $-\nabla p$ in Equation (3.1) by the expression (3.2), and taking account of Equations (3.3) and (3.6), we arrive at

$$\rho\frac{d\mathbf{u}}{dt} = -\nabla p + \rho\mathbf{F} + \left[\frac{\partial}{\partial x}(\tau_{xx}) + \frac{\partial}{\partial y}(\tau_{xy}) + \frac{\partial}{\partial z}(\tau_{xz})\right]\mathbf{i}$$

$$+ \left[\frac{\partial}{\partial x}(\tau_{xy}) + \frac{\partial}{\partial y}(\tau_{yy}) + \frac{\partial}{\partial z}(\tau_{yz})\right]\mathbf{j}$$

$$+ \left[\frac{\partial}{\partial x}(\tau_{xz}) + \frac{\partial}{\partial y}(\tau_{yz}) + \frac{\partial}{\partial z}(\tau_{zz})\right]\mathbf{k}. \qquad (3.7)$$

This is known as *Cauchy's equation*. It specifies conditions to be satisfied by the flow velocity $\mathbf{u}$ in terms of the stress components in the matrix (3.5), which are yet to be specified.

It is only at this point that the model for a Newtonian fluid is introduced, and as you will see in Subsection 3.2, another choice may be made when the flow under consideration is turbulent. The general specification for the stress components in a Newtonian fluid, where $\mathbf{u} = u\,\mathbf{i} + v\,\mathbf{j} + w\,\mathbf{k}$, is

$$\left.\begin{aligned}
\tau_{xx} &= 2\mu\frac{\partial u}{\partial x}, \qquad \tau_{yy} = 2\mu\frac{\partial v}{\partial y}, \qquad \tau_{zz} = 2\mu\frac{\partial w}{\partial z}, \\
\tau_{xy} &= \tau_{yx} = \mu\left(\frac{\partial v}{\partial x} + \frac{\partial u}{\partial y}\right), \\
\tau_{xz} &= \tau_{zx} = \mu\left(\frac{\partial w}{\partial x} + \frac{\partial u}{\partial z}\right), \\
\tau_{yz} &= \tau_{zy} = \mu\left(\frac{\partial w}{\partial y} + \frac{\partial v}{\partial z}\right).
\end{aligned}\right\} \qquad (3.8)$$

This choice embodies the necessary symmetry for the matrix (3.5). It also meets the conditions that

(a) each element of the matrix should be a linear function of the velocity gradients $\partial u/\partial x$, $\partial u/\partial y$, etc.;

(b) each element of the matrix is zero if the fluid block does not undergo any deformation;

(c) no preferred direction in space is implied.

For the shear flow of *Unit 8* Subsection 1.3, where $\mathbf{u} = u(z,t)\,\mathbf{i}$, we have $\tau_{xz} = \tau_{zx} = \mu\,\partial u/\partial z$ as before, with all other stress components equal to zero.

In *Unit 8*, τ_{xz} and τ_{zx} were called σ and τ, respectively.

Exercise 3.1

(a) Verify that the choice of stress components given by Equations (3.8) satisfies the condition (3.4), recalling that the fluid is incompressible.

(b) Verify that the specification (3.8), when applied to Equation (3.7), gives the Navier–Stokes equation

$$\rho\frac{d\mathbf{u}}{dt} = -\nabla p + \rho\mathbf{F} + \mu\nabla^2\mathbf{u}. \qquad (3.9)$$

(Just check the x-component equation in detail.)

3.2 Deriving the RANS equations

Principally because of the non-linearity of the Navier–Stokes equations, the solutions of these equations for given initial and boundary conditions need not be unique. As a result, the equations can accommodate the random fluctuations at higher Reynolds numbers that are known as turbulence, and solutions that are initially steady can become unsteady.

Since the random fluctuations introduce an additional level of complexity that cannot readily be tackled in full detail, we proceed by seeking a time-averaged picture of the full turbulent motion. Suppose that the fluctuations take place over a time scale T which is large enough to capture all of the rapid variation but still small enough to permit the time-averaged velocity to be considered as a function of time, as illustrated in Figure 3.2.

A major difficulty in solving the Navier–Stokes equations for turbulent flows is the very wide range of spatial and temporal scales involved in the motion. This explains the focus on the mean flow.

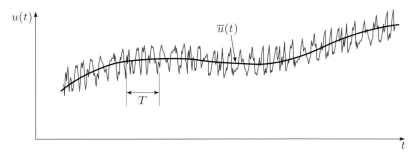

Figure 3.2

The x-component of the flow velocity $\mathbf{u}$ has a mean value defined by

$$\overline{u}(t) = \frac{1}{T} \int_{t-T/2}^{t+T/2} u(s)\, ds, \tag{3.10}$$

where the dependence of u and $\overline{u}$ on x, y and z is implicit throughout. What remains once the mean value $\overline{u}$ has been subtracted from u is the random fluctuation u', which is a rapidly varying but continuous function; that is, $u' = u - \overline{u}$. Averaging $\overline{u}$ a second time has no further effect, since the localised time variation has already been 'ironed out', so that $\overline{\overline{u}} = \overline{u}$. It follows that

Throughout this section, the prime denotes a fluctuating quantity, rather than a derivative.

$$\overline{u'} = \overline{u - \overline{u}} = \overline{u} - \overline{\overline{u}} = \overline{u} - \overline{u} = 0,$$

showing that the mean of the random fluctuations over the averaging time scale is zero. The same applies to other variables of the flow; hence we have

$$u = \overline{u} + u', \qquad v = \overline{v} + v', \qquad w = \overline{w} + w', \qquad p = \overline{p} + p', \tag{3.11}$$

The flow is assumed to be incompressible, so that $\overline{\rho} = \rho$.

with

$$\overline{u'} = \overline{v'} = \overline{w'} = \overline{p'} = 0.$$

The time-averaging satisfies some simple rules, all of which follow from the definition (3.10). If f and g are variables of the flow, with

$$f = \overline{f} + f' \qquad \text{and} \qquad g = \overline{g} + g',$$

then

$$\overline{\overline{f}} = \overline{f}, \qquad \overline{f + g} = \overline{f} + \overline{g}, \qquad \overline{\overline{f}g} = \overline{f}\,\overline{g}.$$

There will be no assessment of the rest of this subsection. It shows how terms such as $-\rho\,\overline{u'v'}$, known as *Reynolds stresses*, contribute to the total shear stress acting on the mean flow. However, it is worth looking at Figure 3.3 and the paragraphs on either side of it.

We also have

$$\overline{\frac{\partial f}{\partial s}} = \frac{\partial \overline{f}}{\partial s}, \qquad \text{where } s \text{ is any of } x, y, z, t.$$

However, it is *not* the case that $\overline{fg} = \overline{f}\,\overline{g}$, since (using the rules above)

$$
\begin{aligned}
\overline{fg} &= \overline{(\overline{f} + f')(\overline{g} + g')} \\
&= \overline{\overline{f}\,\overline{g} + f'\overline{g} + \overline{f}g' + f'g'} \\
&= \overline{\overline{f}\,\overline{g}} + \overline{f'\overline{g}} + \overline{\overline{f}g'} + \overline{f'g'} \\
&= \overline{f}\,\overline{\overline{g}} + \overline{f'}\,\overline{g} + \overline{f}\,\overline{g'} + \overline{f'g'} \\
&= \overline{f}\,\overline{g} + \overline{f'g'} \qquad (\text{since } \overline{f'} = \overline{g'} = 0).
\end{aligned}
\tag{3.12}
$$

This applies in particular when $f = g$:

$$\overline{f^2} = \overline{f}^2 + \overline{f'^2}.$$

Note that $\overline{f'g'}$ need not be zero, even though $\overline{f'} = \overline{g'} = 0$.

The continuity equation for an incompressible fluid is

$$\frac{\partial u}{\partial x} + \frac{\partial v}{\partial y} + \frac{\partial w}{\partial z} = 0, \tag{3.13}$$

where $\mathbf{u} = u\,\mathbf{i} + v\,\mathbf{j} + w\,\mathbf{k}$. Averaging the left-hand side and applying rules from above gives

$$\frac{\partial \overline{u}}{\partial x} + \frac{\partial \overline{v}}{\partial y} + \frac{\partial \overline{w}}{\partial z} = 0. \tag{3.14}$$

On subtracting Equation (3.14) from Equation (3.13), and using the definitions (3.11), we also have

$$\frac{\partial u'}{\partial x} + \frac{\partial v'}{\partial y} + \frac{\partial w'}{\partial z} = 0. \tag{3.15}$$

Hence the continuity equation is satisfied independently by the time-averaged velocity and by the random fluctuations of velocity.

The x-component of the Navier–Stokes equations, when written out in full but without body forces, is

$$\rho\left(\frac{\partial u}{\partial t} + u\frac{\partial u}{\partial x} + v\frac{\partial u}{\partial y} + w\frac{\partial u}{\partial z}\right) = -\frac{\partial p}{\partial x} + \mu\left(\frac{\partial^2 u}{\partial x^2} + \frac{\partial^2 u}{\partial y^2} + \frac{\partial^2 u}{\partial z^2}\right). \tag{3.16}$$

On multiplying the continuity equation (3.13) by ρu, we have

$$\rho\left(u\frac{\partial u}{\partial x} + u\frac{\partial v}{\partial y} + u\frac{\partial w}{\partial z}\right) = 0,$$

and adding this to Equation (3.16) gives

$$\rho\left(\frac{\partial u}{\partial t} + \frac{\partial(u^2)}{\partial x} + \frac{\partial(uv)}{\partial y} + \frac{\partial(uw)}{\partial z}\right) = -\frac{\partial p}{\partial x} + \mu\left(\frac{\partial^2 u}{\partial x^2} + \frac{\partial^2 u}{\partial y^2} + \frac{\partial^2 u}{\partial z^2}\right).$$

Putting $u = \overline{u} + u'$ etc., as in Equations (3.11), leads to

$$
\begin{aligned}
\rho\Bigg(&\frac{\partial \overline{u}}{\partial t} + \frac{\partial u'}{\partial t} + \frac{\partial(\overline{u}^2)}{\partial x} + 2\frac{\partial(\overline{u}u')}{\partial x} + \frac{\partial(u'^2)}{\partial x} + \frac{\partial(\overline{u}\,\overline{v})}{\partial y} + \frac{\partial(\overline{u}v')}{\partial y} + \frac{\partial(u'\overline{v})}{\partial y} \\
&+ \frac{\partial(u'v')}{\partial y} + \frac{\partial(\overline{u}\,\overline{w})}{\partial z} + \frac{\partial(\overline{u}w')}{\partial z} + \frac{\partial(u'\overline{w})}{\partial z} + \frac{\partial(u'w')}{\partial z}\Bigg) \\
&= -\frac{\partial \overline{p}}{\partial x} - \frac{\partial p'}{\partial x} + \mu\left(\frac{\partial^2 \overline{u}}{\partial x^2} + \frac{\partial^2 \overline{u}}{\partial y^2} + \frac{\partial^2 \overline{u}}{\partial z^2}\right) + \mu\left(\frac{\partial^2 u'}{\partial x^2} + \frac{\partial^2 u'}{\partial y^2} + \frac{\partial^2 u'}{\partial z^2}\right).
\end{aligned}
$$

On time-averaging this equation, taking account of the various rules for the process stated above, we obtain

$$\rho\left(\frac{\partial \overline{u}}{\partial t} + \frac{\partial\left(\overline{u}^2\right)}{\partial x} + \frac{\partial\left(\overline{u'^2}\right)}{\partial x} + \frac{\partial\left(\overline{u}\,\overline{v}\right)}{\partial y} + \frac{\partial\left(\overline{u'v'}\right)}{\partial y} + \frac{\partial\left(\overline{u}\,\overline{w}\right)}{\partial z} + \frac{\partial\left(\overline{u'w'}\right)}{\partial z}\right)$$

$$= -\frac{\partial \overline{p}}{\partial x} + \mu\left(\frac{\partial^2 \overline{u}}{\partial x^2} + \frac{\partial^2 \overline{u}}{\partial y^2} + \frac{\partial^2 \overline{u}}{\partial z^2}\right). \tag{3.17}$$

Terms that are linear in u', v', w' vanish under time-averaging, but terms involving products of these quantities do not.

Multiplying the time-averaged continuity equation (3.14) by $\rho\,\overline{u}$ gives

$$\rho\left(\overline{u}\frac{\partial \overline{u}}{\partial x} + \overline{u}\frac{\partial \overline{v}}{\partial y} + \overline{u}\frac{\partial \overline{w}}{\partial z}\right) = 0.$$

Subtracting this from Equation (3.17), and moving the terms involving primed quantities to the right-hand side, we have

$$\rho\left(\frac{\partial \overline{u}}{\partial t} + \overline{u}\frac{\partial \overline{u}}{\partial x} + \overline{v}\frac{\partial \overline{u}}{\partial y} + \overline{w}\frac{\partial \overline{u}}{\partial z}\right) = -\frac{\partial \overline{p}}{\partial x} + \frac{\partial}{\partial x}\left(\mu\frac{\partial \overline{u}}{\partial x} - \rho\,\overline{u'^2}\right)$$

$$+ \frac{\partial}{\partial y}\left(\mu\frac{\partial \overline{u}}{\partial y} - \rho\,\overline{u'v'}\right) + \frac{\partial}{\partial z}\left(\mu\frac{\partial \overline{u}}{\partial z} - \rho\,\overline{u'w'}\right). \tag{3.18}$$

Similar equations can be derived starting from the y- and z-components of the Navier–Stokes equations. Together with Equation (3.18), these are known as the **Reynolds-averaged Navier–Stokes (RANS) equations**.

Using the time-averaged continuity equation (3.14) once more, we have

$$\frac{\partial}{\partial x}\left(\frac{\partial \overline{u}}{\partial x} + \frac{\partial \overline{v}}{\partial y} + \frac{\partial \overline{w}}{\partial z}\right) = \frac{\partial}{\partial x}\left(\frac{\partial \overline{u}}{\partial x}\right) + \frac{\partial}{\partial y}\left(\frac{\partial \overline{v}}{\partial x}\right) + \frac{\partial}{\partial z}\left(\frac{\partial \overline{w}}{\partial x}\right) = 0.$$

Writing

$$\overline{\tau}_{xx} = 2\mu\frac{\partial \overline{u}}{\partial x}, \quad \overline{\tau}_{xy} = \mu\left(\frac{\partial \overline{v}}{\partial x} + \frac{\partial \overline{u}}{\partial y}\right), \quad \overline{\tau}_{xz} = \mu\left(\frac{\partial \overline{w}}{\partial x} + \frac{\partial \overline{u}}{\partial z}\right), \tag{3.19}$$

Equation (3.18) can now be written as

$$\rho\left(\frac{\partial \overline{u}}{\partial t} + (\overline{\mathbf{u}} \cdot \boldsymbol{\nabla})\,\overline{u}\right) = -\frac{\partial \overline{p}}{\partial x} + \frac{\partial}{\partial x}\left(\overline{\tau}_{xx} - \rho\,\overline{u'^2}\right) + \frac{\partial}{\partial y}\left(\overline{\tau}_{xy} - \rho\,\overline{u'v'}\right)$$

$$+ \frac{\partial}{\partial z}\left(\overline{\tau}_{xz} - \rho\,\overline{u'w'}\right).$$

Here $\overline{\mathbf{u}} = \overline{u}\,\mathbf{i} + \overline{v}\,\mathbf{j} + \overline{w}\,\mathbf{k}$.

This can be recognised as the x-component of Cauchy's equation (3.7), with $\overline{u}$ in place of u and with shear stresses

$$\tau_{xx} = \overline{\tau}_{xx} - \rho\,\overline{u'^2}, \qquad \tau_{xy} = \overline{\tau}_{xy} - \rho\,\overline{u'v'}, \qquad \tau_{xz} = \overline{\tau}_{xz} - \rho\,\overline{u'w'}.$$

On comparing Equations (3.19) and (3.8), it can be seen that $\overline{\tau}_{xx}$, $\overline{\tau}_{xy}$, $\overline{\tau}_{xz}$ are the shear stresses arising from viscous action according to the Newtonian model. The further terms $-\rho\,\overline{u'^2}$, $-\rho\,\overline{u'v'}$, $-\rho\,\overline{u'w'}$ (and their counterparts in the other two RANS equations) can therefore be identified as additional shear stress contributions due to the random fluctuations of the turbulent motion; they are known as *Reynolds stresses*.

Reynolds derived these expressions for turbulent shear stress in 1894.

Exercise 3.2

Verify that the expressions for the Reynolds stresses have the dimensions of a stress (force per unit area).

On putting

$$\tau_{xx} = \overline{\tau}_{xx} + \tau'_{xx}, \qquad \tau_{xy} = \overline{\tau}_{xy} + \tau'_{xy}, \qquad \tau_{xz} = \overline{\tau}_{xz} + \tau'_{xz}, \qquad \text{etc.},$$

the Reynolds stresses are given in full by

$$\begin{pmatrix} \tau'_{xx} & \tau'_{xy} & \tau'_{xz} \\ \tau'_{yx} & \tau'_{yy} & \tau'_{yz} \\ \tau'_{zx} & \tau'_{zy} & \tau'_{zz} \end{pmatrix} = -\rho \begin{pmatrix} \overline{u'^2} & \overline{u'v'} & \overline{u'w'} \\ \overline{u'v'} & \overline{v'^2} & \overline{v'w'} \\ \overline{u'w'} & \overline{v'w'} & \overline{w'^2} \end{pmatrix}. \qquad (3.20)$$

See the *Media Guide* for more on the derivation of the RANS equations and interpretation of the Reynolds stresses.

It is clear that the matrix (3.5) of shear stress components remains symmetric with this assignment.

In most parts of a flow that is turbulent, the Reynolds stresses (3.20) are far greater in magnitude than the corresponding viscous stresses (3.19). An exception is in the immediate vicinity of a solid boundary, where the random fluctuations of turbulence are inhibited by the presence of the boundary. Where the Reynolds stresses dominate, the effect on the mean flow is as if the viscosity were many times greater than it actually is, so that flow with a given pressure gradient is much more significantly impeded. A greater pressure drop is therefore required over a given length of pipe in order to achieve a specified flow rate along the pipe. This is illustrated in Figure 3.3(a), which shows the velocity profiles across a pipe for laminar and turbulent mean flow, where the pressure gradient is the same in each case. Figure 3.3(b) shows an alternative comparison where the mean velocity across the pipe is the same in each case.

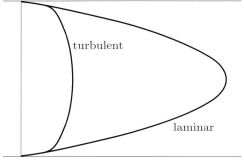
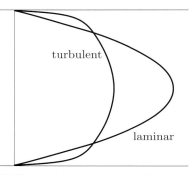

(a) Flow with same pressure gradient   (b) Flow with same mean velocity

Figure 3.3

The velocity profiles in the boundary layer for external flow past a plate are similarly steeper for turbulent than for laminar flow when close to the boundary (where viscosity has an effect) but flatter further out, where the Reynolds stresses dominate.

3.3 Momentum integral equation for turbulent flow

Boundary layer equations

In Subsection 2.1 we derived the boundary layer equations for steady, incompressible, two-dimensional flow past a fixed flat plate. We did this by starting from the Navier–Stokes equations (2.2) and (2.3), then making appropriate approximations, based on the dimensionless form of the equations. The outcome was given by Equation (2.9) together with the continuity equation (2.1).

A similar process can be undertaken starting from the RANS equations, noting that the only difference in the structure of the equations is due to the presence of the Reynolds stresses. Another approach is to start from the boundary layer equation (2.7), put $u = \overline{u} + u'$, $v = \overline{v} + v'$ and $p = \overline{p} + p'$, then time-average the result. In either case, the outcome is

$$\overline{u}\frac{\partial \overline{u}}{\partial x} + \overline{v}\frac{\partial \overline{u}}{\partial y} = -\frac{1}{\rho}\frac{dp}{dx} + \frac{1}{\rho}\frac{\partial \tau}{\partial y}, \tag{3.21}$$

where

$$\tau = \tau_v + \tau_t, \qquad \tau_v = \overline{\tau}_{xy} = \mu\frac{\partial \overline{u}}{\partial y}, \qquad \tau_t = \tau'_{xy} = -\rho\,\overline{u'v'}. \tag{3.22}$$

The subscripts on τ_v and τ_t denote viscous and turbulent stresses, respectively. We put

$$\overline{\tau}_{xy} = \mu\frac{\partial \overline{u}}{\partial y}$$

rather than

$$\overline{\tau}_{xy} = \mu\left(\frac{\partial \overline{u}}{\partial y} + \frac{\partial \overline{v}}{\partial x}\right),$$

This equation and the continuity equation, $\partial \overline{u}/\partial x + \partial \overline{v}/\partial y = 0$, together constitute the *boundary layer equations* for the mean velocity of a turbulent flow.

The pressure is still essentially constant across the boundary layer, with

$$\frac{dp}{dx} = -\rho U\frac{dU}{dx} \tag{3.23}$$

as in Equations (3.8), because the dimensionless form shows $\partial \overline{v}/\partial x$ to be negligible compared with $\partial \overline{u}/\partial y$.

as in Equation (2.8), where p is the pressure external to the boundary layer, and U is the external flow velocity parallel to the plate.

If $\partial \overline{u}/\partial y > 0$, as is the case in an unseparated boundary layer, then the viscous shear stress term $\tau_v = \mu\,\partial \overline{u}/\partial y$ will be positive. We now argue that the same must be true for the Reynolds stress $\tau_t = -\rho\,\overline{u'v'}$. This is the case because, on average, the quantity $u'v'$ can be expected to be negative.

Consider the mean shear flow with $\overline{\mathbf{u}} = \overline{u}(y)\,\mathbf{i}$ and $\partial \overline{u}/\partial y > 0$, shown in Figure 3.4. The transverse motion due to turbulence causes eddies to approach the level AB from above and below. Those arriving from below (hence with $v' > 0$) come from a region of smaller $\overline{u}$, and since they essentially retain their initial velocity, their u' at the level AB is less than it was below; on average, the resulting u' values will be negative. On the other hand, eddies approaching the level AB from above (with $v' < 0$) come from a region of larger $\overline{u}$, and so provide u' values at the level AB that are greater than they were above, and on average positive. Hence the average $\overline{u'v'}$ is negative, and $\tau_t = -\rho\,\overline{u'v'} > 0$.

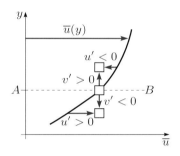

Figure 3.4

Momentum integral equation

The *momentum integral equation* for turbulent flow follows from the boundary layer equations just as for the laminar case in Subsection 2.2, that is,

$$\frac{d\delta_2}{dx} + (\delta_1 + 2\delta_2)\frac{1}{U}\frac{dU}{dx} = \frac{\tau_0}{\rho U^2}, \tag{3.24}$$

This is Equation (2.13).

where

$$\delta_1(x) = \int_0^h \left(1 - \frac{\overline{u}}{U}\right)dy,$$

$$\delta_2(x) = \int_0^h \frac{\overline{u}}{U}\left(1 - \frac{\overline{u}}{U}\right)dy,$$

These are Equation (2.14), for the displacement thickness, and Equation (2.15), for the momentum thickness, with $\overline{u}$ in place of u. As in the laminar case, if a finite boundary layer thickness δ is assumed, then $h = \delta$ can be taken.

and $\tau_0 = [\tau]_{y=0}$. Both the mean and fluctuating parts of the velocity must individually satisfy the boundary conditions at $y = 0$, that is,

$$\overline{u} = \overline{v} = 0 \quad \text{and} \quad u' = v' = 0 \quad \text{at } y = 0.$$

Hence $[\tau_t]_{y=0} = 0$ and so $\tau_0 = [\tau_v]_{y=0} = \mu[\partial \overline{u}/\partial y]_{y=0}$.

Consider the case of zero external pressure gradient, so $dU/dx = 0$ from Equation (3.23). The exact solution to the boundary layer equations in the laminar case, found in Subsection 2.3, has no counterpart for turbulent flow. We are therefore forced back on the approach of trying mean velocity profiles which look reasonable from an empirical point of view. This time we concentrate less on meeting the boundary conditions of the problem and more on trying to replicate the overall shape of the velocity profile. This leads to suggested velocity profiles of the form

$$\frac{\overline{u}}{U} = \left(\frac{y}{\delta}\right)^{1/n} \qquad \left(0 \leq \frac{y}{\delta} \leq 1\right), \tag{3.25}$$

where $n \geq 6$ is an integer that depends on the Reynolds number but is assumed to be constant for a range of Reynolds numbers. The shape of this graph, shown in Figure 3.5, roughly replicates the features for turbulent flow noted after Figure 3.3.

This function satisfies the boundary conditions $\overline{u} = 0$ at $y = 0$ and $\overline{u} = U$ at $y = \delta$, but not the other boundary conditions.

Corresponding to $Re = 10^6$, we take $n = 7$ in Equation (3.25). In the absence of the relationship $\tau = \mu \, \partial u/\partial y$ that holds across the boundary layer in the laminar case, we require a separate specification of τ_0. We take

$$\tau_0 = \frac{0.0225\rho U^2}{(U\delta/\nu)^{1/4}}, \tag{3.26}$$

which was formulated first from experiments to measure the resistance to flow in smooth pipes.

The choice $n = 7$ holds reasonably well for a range of $Re = UL/\nu$ from 5×10^5 to 10^7, but is often applied for higher Re too. For pipe flow, the range of validity is about $5 \times 10^3 < Re < 2 \times 10^5$.

Exercise 3.3

(a) Find the displacement thickness δ_1 and momentum thickness δ_2 corresponding to the velocity profile

$$\frac{\overline{u}}{U} = \left(\frac{y}{\delta}\right)^{1/7} \qquad \left(0 \leq \frac{y}{\delta} \leq 1\right),$$

for water flow over a flat plate with zero external pressure gradient.

(b) Using Equation (3.26) and the momentum integral equation (3.24), show that

$$\frac{\delta}{x} = \frac{0.371}{(Ux/\nu)^{1/5}},$$

and that the total skin friction drag per unit breadth on a plate of length L is

$$F_L = \frac{0.0360\rho U^2 L}{(UL/\nu)^{1/5}}.$$

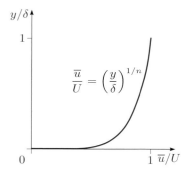

Figure 3.5   Here $n = 7$

Exercise 3.4

Water flows at a rate of $1.6\,\mathrm{m^3\,s^{-1}}$ down a channel of length $8.0\,\mathrm{m}$ with a rectangular cross-section of breadth $2.0\,\mathrm{m}$. The depth of water is $0.4\,\mathrm{m}$.

(a) Estimate the displacement thickness at the end of the channel, assuming that a turbulent boundary layer starts at the entrance to the channel and the one-seventh power law applies for the velocity profile within the boundary layer.

(b) Find the percentage reduction in effective cross-sectional area at the end of the channel, taking the boundary layers into account on both the bed and the side walls of the channel.

For water, take $\nu = 1.0 \times 10^{-6}\,\mathrm{m^2\,s^{-1}}$.

The 'one-seventh power law' should be taken as including the specification of τ_0 in Equation (3.26).

Following Exercise 3.3, we are in a position to compare the results for a turbulent model, based mainly on empirical data, with those for the laminar model obtained by solving the Blasius equation in Subsection 2.3. The results are shown in Table 3.1.

Table 3.1   Comparison of laminar and turbulent boundary layers

quantity	laminar (Blasius)	turbulent ($\frac{1}{7}$ power law)
δ	$5x(Re_x)^{-1/2} \propto x^{1/2}$	$0.371x(Re_x)^{-1/5} \propto x^{4/5}$
δ_1	$0.344\delta \propto x^{1/2}$	$\frac{1}{8}\delta \propto x^{4/5}$
δ_2	$0.133\delta \propto x^{1/2}$	$\frac{7}{72}\delta \propto x^{4/5}$
τ_0	$0.332\rho U^2(Re_x)^{-1/2} \propto x^{-1/2}$	$0.0288\rho U^2(Re_x)^{-1/5} \propto x^{-1/5}$
F_L	$0.664\rho U^2 L(Re_L)^{-1/2} \propto L^{1/2}$	$0.0360\rho U^2 L(Re_L)^{-1/5} \propto L^{4/5}$

Here $Re_x = Ux/\nu$ and $Re_L = UL/\nu$, while F_L is the total skin friction drag force per unit breadth.

These results show that the thickness of a turbulent boundary layer grows more rapidly, with distance along the plate, than that of a laminar boundary layer (at a rate proportional to $x^{4/5}$ rather than $x^{1/2}$); this is confirmed experimentally. For small values of Re_x and Re_L, the predictions for laminar flow are larger for δ, δ_1, δ_2, τ_0 and F_L, but for the values of Reynolds number encountered in most practical cases, the turbulent boundary layer is thicker and the drag force greater than would be the case for laminar flow.

Exercise 3.5

(a) Find the value of Re_x for which the shear stresses predicted for laminar and turbulent flow in Table 3.1 are equal.

(b) Find the value of Re_L for which the total skin friction drag forces predicted for laminar and turbulent flow in Table 3.1 are equal.

The transition from laminar to turbulent flow past a flat plate takes place at about $Re_x = 5 \times 10^5$, and so in practice the drag caused by a turbulent flow is far greater than that for an equivalent laminar flow. Consequently, the sooner the transition from laminar to turbulent flow takes place for flow past a body, the greater the overall skin friction drag on the body will be. However, turbulent boundary layers take a greater distance to separate from the surface of the body (if they do so at all) in comparison to their laminar counterparts, and early separation of the boundary layer leads to an increase in profile drag. An early transition from laminar to turbulent flow can therefore reduce the profile drag and hence also the overall drag, despite the resulting increase in skin friction drag.

Exercise 3.6

A smooth rectangular flat plate, with sides of length p and $4p$, is held parallel to a uniform stream. Assuming that flow in the boundary layer is turbulent throughout, state whether the total skin friction drag is greater when the shorter side is held parallel to the direction of flow or when the longer side is parallel to the flow.

After seeking a qualitative answer by physical reasoning, calculate the ratio of the two drag forces. Use the results given in Table 3.1 that correspond to the one-seventh power law for the velocity profile.

This is the same question as for Exercise 2.4, but now for turbulent rather than laminar flow.

Exercise 3.7

A train of length $210 \, \text{m}$ travels at $56 \, \text{m s}^{-1}$ ($125 \, \text{mph}$). The train is $2.75 \, \text{m}$ wide and $4.0 \, \text{m}$ high, so that the skin friction on the sides and top is equivalent to that on a flat plate of breadth $10.75 \, \text{m}$. Friction on the bottom surface of the train is to be neglected.

(a) Using the results given in Table 3.1 for the one-seventh power law for the velocity profile, estimate the power (total drag force × speed, in kW) required to overcome the frictional resistance on the train.

(b) Calculate the maximum thickness of the boundary layer on the train.

(c) How do the results obtained in parts (a) and (b) compare with those for a hypothetical laminar boundary layer in the same situation?

For air, take $\mu = 1.80 \times 10^{-5} \, \text{kg m}^{-1} \text{s}^{-1}$ and $\rho = 1.20 \, \text{kg m}^{-3}$.

3.4   Kinematic eddy viscosity and mixing length

The RANS equations (one of which is Equation (3.18)), together with the continuity equation, are to be used to compute solutions for the time-averaged velocity $\overline{\mathbf{u}} = \overline{u} \, \mathbf{i} + \overline{v} \, \mathbf{j} + \overline{w} \, \mathbf{k}$ and pressure $\overline{p}$. However, as things stand we have insufficient information to solve these equations (even numerically, as would usually be the case), because there are further unknown quantities beyond those that we wish to solve for, namely, the Reynolds stresses.

The original Navier–Stokes equations rely additionally on the Newtonian model of viscosity, which replaces shear stresses by derivatives of velocity components and so 'closes' the system of equations. For the RANS equations we require some principle that will similarly permit closure of the equations, by relating the Reynolds stresses,

$$\tau'_{xx} = -\rho \, \overline{u'^{\,2}}, \qquad \tau'_{xy} = -\rho \, \overline{u'v'}, \qquad \text{etc.,}$$

to derivatives of the time-averaged velocity components, $\overline{u}$, $\overline{v}$ and $\overline{w}$. A linkage of this type between the Reynolds stresses and mean velocity components is called a *turbulence model*. Several such models have been proposed, but only one will be considered here. Moreover, we continue to confine attention to shear flow in a boundary layer or pipe.

By analogy with the Newtonian viscosity model, which states that

$$\tau_v = \overline{\tau}_{xy} = \rho \nu \frac{\partial \overline{u}}{\partial y}, \qquad \text{where } \nu = \frac{\mu}{\rho}, \qquad\qquad \text{See Equations (3.22).}$$

Joseph Boussinesq (in 1877) proposed that the additional apparent stresses caused by turbulence could be modelled by expressions such as

$$\tau_t = \tau'_{xy} = -\rho \, \overline{u'v'} = \rho \nu_t \frac{\partial \overline{u}}{\partial y}, \qquad (3.27)$$

where ν_t is the *kinematic eddy viscosity*. Here ν_t is not a property of the fluid as such (which ν is) but a property of the flow; indeed it is zero if the flow is not turbulent. Consequently ν_t can vary from place to place, even if the time-averaged flow is steady.

For the general RANS equation (3.18), this would read

$$\tau'_{xy} = \rho \nu_t \left(\frac{\partial \overline{u}}{\partial y} + \frac{\partial \overline{v}}{\partial x} \right),$$

etc. Also $\mu_t = \rho \nu_t$ is called the *eddy viscosity*.

On the face of it, all that has been done so far is to shift the problem of modelling τ_t to the problem of modelling ν_t, but this turns out to be some advance since the latter is easier to model.

In 1925 Prandtl proposed a distribution law for the kinematic eddy viscosity based on the idea of a *mixing length*. By analogy to the molecular motion of gases, Prandtl assumed a simplified model of turbulent fluctuations, in which individual parcels of fluid are displaced with the fluctuations by a mean distance l_m, the *mixing length*. In the case where l_m is regarded as perpendicular to the main flow direction, the fluid parcels retain their momentum. This is illustrated schematically in Figure 3.6.

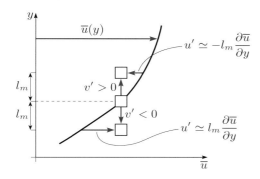

Figure 3.6

Assume that, as shown, $\partial \overline{u} / \partial y > 0$. A fluid parcel which moves from y to $y + l_m$ (hence with $v' > 0$) has a lower velocity than its new surroundings, with

$$u' \simeq - [\overline{u}(y + l_m) - \overline{u}(y)] \simeq -l_m \frac{\partial \overline{u}}{\partial y},$$

while a parcel moving from y to $y - l_m$ (with $v' < 0$) has a higher velocity locally, with

$$u' \simeq \overline{u}(y) - \overline{u}(y - l_m) \simeq l_m \frac{\partial \overline{u}}{\partial y}.$$

> This quantifies the argument given on page 97 to show that $\tau_t = -\rho \,\overline{u'v'}$ is positive.

Assuming that u' and v' have the same order of magnitude, Prandtl then formulated the Reynolds stress as

$$\tau_t = \tau'_{xy} = -\rho \,\overline{u'v'} = \rho l_m^2 \frac{\partial \overline{u}}{\partial y} \left| \frac{\partial \overline{u}}{\partial y} \right|, \tag{3.28}$$

where the modulus sign ensures that $\tau_t > 0$ for $\partial \overline{u} / \partial y > 0$, and $\tau_t < 0$ for $\partial \overline{u} / \partial y < 0$. Comparing Equations (3.27) and (3.28), we have the expression

$$\nu_t = l_m^2 \left| \frac{\partial \overline{u}}{\partial y} \right|$$

for the kinematic eddy viscosity. This equation is important because it is easier to suggest suitable distributions for the mixing length l_m than for ν_t. Near a solid surface the size of eddies will be smaller, so that $l_m \to 0$ as a solid boundary is approached, while more generally in the shear flow considered, l_m will be a function of the distance y away from the boundary.

A simple assumption for turbulent flow near a flat plate is that $l_m = \kappa y$, where κ is a dimensionless constant (known as the *Kármán constant*) whose value turns out to be about 0.4. This same assumption can also be applied within a pipe, with y again measuring distance away from the wall, so that $y = a - r$ for a pipe with radius a and radial coordinate r.

At the centre of a pipe, the mixing length can be expected to be a maximum. For flow over a flat plate there will again be a maximum mixing length l_m within the boundary layer, but also $l_m \to 0$ as y increases towards the edge of the boundary layer, since the flow outside is inviscid.

An instructive case is that of turbulent flow in an open channel with constant pressure gradient. Here it can be shown that the shear stress varies linearly with depth in the channel. With the velocity profile chosen in a manner to be described in Section 4, it can also be shown that the profiles of the mixing length l_m and kinematic eddy viscosity ν_t are as in Figure 3.7.

The argument to show linearity here is similar to that used for a pipe following Exercise 2.7.

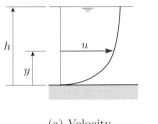

(a) Velocity

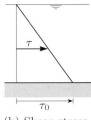

(b) Shear stress

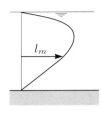

(c) Mixing length

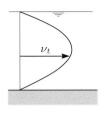

(d) Kinematic eddy viscosity

Figure 3.7

End-of-section exercise

Exercise 3.8

For Reynolds numbers $Re_L = UL/\nu$ in the range from 10^6 to 10^8, experimental data suggest a power law velocity profile for flow past a flat plate with zero external pressure gradient of the form

$$\frac{\overline{u}}{U} = \left(\frac{y}{\delta}\right)^{1/9} \qquad \left(0 \le \frac{y}{\delta} \le 1\right),$$

while data on frictional resistance indicate that

$$\tau_0 = \frac{0.0145\rho U^2}{(U\delta/\nu)^{1/5}}.$$

(a) Find the displacement thickness δ_1 and momentum thickness δ_2 in this case.

(b) Use the momentum integral equation (3.24) to show that

$$\frac{\delta}{x} = \frac{0.275}{(Ux/\nu)^{1/6}},$$

and that the total skin friction drag per unit breadth on a plate of length L is

$$F_L = \frac{0.0225\rho U^2 L}{(UL/\nu)^{1/6}}.$$

(c) Apply these results to rework Exercise 3.7(a) and (b).

4 Turbulent boundary layers

The suggested velocity profiles of the form $\overline{u}/U = (y/\delta)^{1/n}$, based on empirical evidence, each hold only for a restricted range of values of the Reynolds number. Moreover, an expression for the shear stress τ_0 at the solid boundary has to be provided separately in each case, in order for progress to be made.

See Equation (3.25).

For $n = 7$, the expression for τ_0 is Equation (3.26).

While these velocity profiles have an important place in practical calculations of the skin friction forces exerted and of boundary layer growth, it would be more satisfactory to have a single theory that encompassed all of the Reynolds numbers to be encountered and also linked the shear stress with the nature of the velocity profile. This section pursues that aim.

Subsection 4.1 investigates what can be said about the overall structure of turbulent boundary layers, arriving at a logarithmic form for much of the velocity profile, and Subsection 4.2 shows how this enables the skin friction coefficient and hence the shear stress at the boundary to be calculated from the Reynolds number. Subsection 4.3 extends the model to include rough as well as smooth surfaces.

While the discussion is initially in terms of flow with zero external pressure gradient past a flat plate, it should also be considered to include fully developed flow within a pipe, with the radius a of the pipe replacing the boundary layer thickness, δ.

In this section, the mean velocity $\overline{u}$ (time-averaged over turbulent perturbations) is denoted simply by u throughout.

4.1 Structure of a turbulent boundary layer

As pointed out in Section 1, the overall structure of a boundary layer is more complex than considered in Sections 2 and 3: there is typically a laminar section followed by a turbulent section, as shown in Figure 4.1.

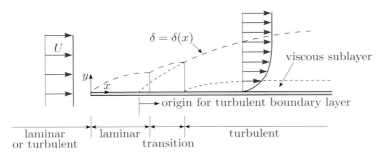

Figure 4.1

The onset of turbulence in the boundary layer is determined by the Reynolds number $Re_x = Ux/\nu$, where x is the distance along the plate, and U is the external stream velocity. Just as, for pipe flow, a value of $Re_d = Ud/\nu$ of 2300 is often taken as the transition point between laminar and turbulent flow, so for flow past a plate the value $Re_x = 5 \times 10^5$ is regarded as critical. (In each case, however, there is considerable variation possible in these figures, depending on external factors.) Transition in the external flow case may in fact take place for $3.2 \times 10^5 < Re_x < 5 \times 10^5$, with laminar flow when $Re_x < 3.2 \times 10^5$ and fully turbulent flow when $Re_x > 5 \times 10^5$. Measurements along a turbulent boundary layer are usually taken from from a 'virtual origin' chosen as shown in Figure 4.1, where the edge of the turbulent boundary layer would meet the plate if extended all the way to $y = 0$.

For Re_d, the velocity U is the mean velocity across the pipe, and d is the pipe diameter.

103

Exercise 4.1

(a) Show that the flow of Exercise 2.5 can be expected to be laminar along the entire length of the plate.

(b) Estimate how far along the train of Exercise 3.7 the transition from laminar to turbulent flow will occur, based on a transition point for $Re_x = 5 \times 10^5$.

We have previously considered boundary layers that are either laminar or turbulent, but as Figure 4.1 illustrates, a real boundary layer is first laminar and then (given a sufficient length of plate) turbulent. Formulas exist to take account of the combination of laminar and turbulent flows that occurs in practice. However, for the cases to be considered here, a boundary layer flow can reasonably be considered to be either all laminar or all turbulent.

We turn now to a more detailed scrutiny of what can be said about turbulent boundary layers. It is observed that, after the boundary layer has become turbulent, there is still a thin *viscous sublayer* within the boundary layer, right next to the plate. In this region the viscosity is important, and the viscous stress increasingly dominates the Reynolds (turbulent) stress as the boundary is approached.

Assuming that $\tau = \mu \, \partial u / \partial y$ in the viscous sublayer (ignoring the Reynolds stress) and that τ is constant here gives

$$\frac{\partial u}{\partial y} = \frac{\tau}{\mu} = \frac{\tau_0}{\mu},$$

where τ_0 is the shear stress at the plate. Hence

$$u = \frac{\tau_0}{\mu} y \tag{4.1}$$

within the viscous sublayer.

The external flow speed, U, and boundary layer thickness, δ, are appropriate speed and length scales for the boundary layer as a whole, but they are not significant for the flow that takes place adjacent to the plate. Here there are other natural scales that can be defined in terms of the locally important parameters, which are τ_0, ρ and ν $(= \mu/\rho)$. Hence we define the *friction velocity*, u_τ, and the *viscous length scale*, δ_ν, by

$$u_\tau = \sqrt{\frac{\tau_0}{\rho}} \quad \text{and} \quad \delta_\nu = \frac{\nu}{u_\tau}. \tag{4.2}$$

Exercise 4.2

Verify that $u_\tau^2 = \tau_0/\rho$ has the dimensions of (speed)^2, and that $\delta_\nu = \nu/u_\tau$ has the dimensions of length.

The scales introduced in Equations (4.2) permit lengths and speeds close to the plate to be measured in *wall units*, that is, as multiples of δ_ν or u_τ.

For example, the velocity profile given by Equation (4.1), within the viscous sublayer, can be rearranged to give the dimensionless velocity u/u_τ in terms of the dimensionless distance y/δ_ν. Since

$$\frac{\tau_0}{\mu} = \frac{\tau_0}{\rho\nu} = \frac{u_\tau^2}{\nu} = \frac{u_\tau}{\delta_\nu},$$

we have

$$\frac{u}{u_\tau} = \frac{y}{\delta_\nu}, \qquad \text{or} \qquad \frac{u}{u_\tau} = \frac{u_\tau y}{\nu}. \qquad (4.3)$$

This velocity profile holds only within the viscous sublayer, which extends outwards from the plate to about $y \simeq 5\delta_\nu$.

Moving away from the viscous sublayer, the turbulent stresses dominate increasingly, and any viscous effects are soon swamped. Following the line of argument originally adopted by Prandtl, suppose that (in a region outside the viscous sublayer but still fairly close to the wall) the shear stress (now due to turbulence) remains constant, while the mixing length is proportional to the distance y from the plate, that is,

$$\tau = \tau_0 \qquad \text{and} \qquad l_m = \kappa y, \qquad (4.4)$$

where κ is a dimensionless constant.

Then, according to Equation (3.28), we have

$$\tau_0 = \rho\kappa^2 y^2 \left(\frac{\partial u}{\partial y}\right)^2 \qquad \left(\text{since } \frac{\partial u}{\partial y} > 0\right), \qquad \text{or}$$

$$\frac{\partial u}{\partial y} = \frac{1}{\kappa}\sqrt{\frac{\tau_0}{\rho}}\frac{1}{y}. \qquad (4.5)$$

Integration and use of $u_\tau = \sqrt{\tau_0/\rho}$ gives

$$\frac{u}{u_\tau} = \frac{1}{\kappa}\ln y + C, \qquad (4.6)$$

where C is a constant. The argument of the logarithm can be rendered dimensionless by the device of subtracting and adding $(1/\kappa)\ln(\nu/u_\tau)$ to the right-hand side, to obtain

$$\frac{u}{u_\tau} = \frac{1}{\kappa}\ln\left(\frac{u_\tau y}{\nu}\right) + B, \qquad \text{where } B = C + \frac{1}{\kappa}\ln\left(\frac{\nu}{u_\tau}\right). \qquad (4.7)$$

The premises on which this result were based, namely Equations (4.4) and (3.28), may give cause for doubt as to the worth of the outcome. Indeed, different assumptions for the forms of τ and l_m may lead to the same result.

Exercise 4.3

Show that if

$$\tau = \tau_0\left(1 - \frac{y}{\delta}\right) \qquad \text{and} \qquad l_m = \kappa y\left(1 - \frac{y}{\delta}\right)^{1/2},$$

then an application of Equation (3.28) leads to Equation (4.5) once more.

There is also a dimensional argument leading to Equation (4.5). In the direction perpendicular to the plate there are two significant length scales, δ and $\delta_\nu = \nu/u_\tau$. Hence the dimensionless velocity u/u_τ can be expected to depend on the dimensionless lengths y/δ and y/δ_ν. However, δ and δ_ν are of different orders of magnitude, and so we expect a relationship of the form $u/u_\tau = f(y/\delta)$ towards the outside of the boundary layer and $u/u_\tau = g(y/\delta_\nu)$ towards the plate.

The limits suggested for the various sublayers within the boundary layer are somewhat arbitrary, and vary to an extent between authors.

To give an idea of the relative magnitudes of u_τ and δ_ν compared with U and δ, a calculation for the back of the train in Exercise 3.7 gives $u_\tau/U \simeq 0.02$ and $\delta_\nu/\delta \simeq 10^{-5}$.

The mixing length was introduced in Subsection 3.4.

These choices are consistent with the linear shear stress distribution for an open channel, seen in Figure 3.7.

Dimensional arguments such as this are important in fluid mechanics in general, but particularly in studies of turbulence.

In the intervening area, neither f nor g is expected to figure strongly. Hence in this region the dimensionless expression $(y/u_\tau)\,\partial u/\partial y$ can depend neither on y/δ nor on y/δ_ν, but must equal a constant ($1/\kappa$, say) independent of either of them. This leads to Equation (4.5) once more.

Whatever the solidity of the argument on which Equation (4.7) rests, it holds up remarkably well when compared with experimental results, for the approximate range of distances $30 < y/\delta_\nu < 1000$. Equation (4.7) can be written as

$$\frac{u}{u_\tau} = A \ln\left(\frac{u_\tau y}{\nu}\right) + B, \qquad \text{with } A = \frac{1}{\kappa}. \tag{4.8}$$

The original value obtained experimentally for the *Kármán constant*, κ, was 0.40, giving $A = 2.50$, while $B = 5.5$ also arises from experiment. Hence we have

The value $\kappa = 0.41$ is also commonly used.

$$\frac{u}{u_\tau} = 2.5 \ln\left(\frac{u_\tau y}{\nu}\right) + 5.5 = 5.75 \log_{10}\left(\frac{u_\tau y}{\nu}\right) + 5.5. \tag{4.9}$$

The values quoted here are widely accepted, though different experiments tend to provide a range of possibilities for A and B. The versions with ln and $\log_{10}$ are both used frequently, for different purposes.

Note that
$$\ln P = \ln(10) \log_{10} P$$
$$\simeq 2.30 \log_{10} P.$$

Equations (4.8) and (4.9) are called the *inner velocity law* or *law of the wall* (even though the range of values of y/δ_ν for which the law applies does not extend to the wall). The region in which these equations hold is sometimes called the *inertial sublayer* and sometimes the *overlap layer*.

Equation (4.9) can also be written as
$$\frac{u}{u_\tau} = 2.5 \ln\left(\frac{9u_\tau y}{\nu}\right)$$
$$= 5.75 \log_{10}\left(\frac{9u_\tau y}{\nu}\right).$$

Figure 4.2 graphs the models obtained for the viscous sublayer (Equation (4.3)) and the inertial sublayer (Equation (4.9)), together with experimental results for both external flow past a flat plate (outline dots) and flow within a pipe (solid dots).

Since the horizontal scale is logarithmic, the graph of Equation (4.9) appears as a straight line, while that for Equation (4.3), a linear function of y, appears curved.

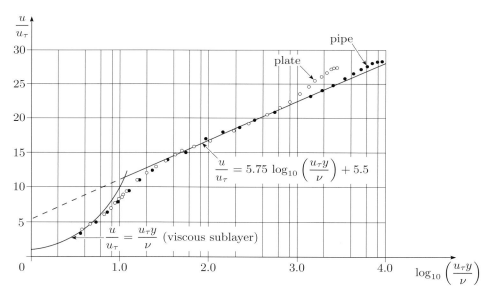

Figure 4.2

It is clear that, while the parts of the model derived so far are validated by experiments, some further work is needed to 'fill in the gap' between the outer edge of the viscous sublayer (at $y \simeq 5\delta_\nu$) and the inner edge of the inertial sublayer (at $y \simeq 30\delta_\nu$). This is a matter of finding an appropriate function for the range of values concerned which will match smoothly onto the other parts of the model at either end, and there are a variety of ways of doing this. One such possibility for $5 \le y/\delta_\nu \le 30$, which 'merges into' the functions on either side, is

$$\frac{u}{u_\tau} = \frac{u_\tau y}{\nu} - 0.04013 \left(\frac{u_\tau y}{\nu} - 5\right)^2 + 5.813 \times 10^{-4} \left(\frac{u_\tau y}{\nu} - 5\right)^3. \qquad (4.10)$$

The region where this equation holds is sometimes called the *buffer layer*.

It can be seen from Figure 4.2 that towards the outside of the boundary layer (or centre of the pipe) the experimental results depart somewhat from the law of the wall (4.9). However, this departure occurs sooner and to a more marked extent for external flow past a plate than it does for flow within a pipe, and for many purposes it is reasonable to model pipe flow by assuming that the logarithmic law of the wall holds all the way to the centre of the pipe. This assumption will be made in calculating the resistance to flow within a pipe in Subsection 4.2.

If you have time, you can check that this matches the velocity and velocity gradient for the inertial sublayer at $u_\tau y/\nu = 30$. The similar match with the viscous sublayer at $u_\tau y/\nu = 5$ is visible from the form of the function.

For an external flow, on the other hand, further attention must be paid to the outer region, between $y/\delta_\nu \simeq 1000$ and the edge of the boundary layer. It is usual to add to the logarithmic expression (4.9) an S-shaped function f which tends to zero as $y/\delta \to 0$ and has derivative zero at $y/\delta = 1$. Then Equation (4.9) is amended to

$$\frac{u}{u_\tau} = 2.5 \ln \left(\frac{u_\tau y}{\nu}\right) + 5.5 + 2.25 f \left(\frac{y}{\delta}\right),$$

where the new constant 2.25 is an experimentally determined value for which $f(1) = 1$. This is known as *Coles' law of the wake*, where f is called a *wake function*. Popular choices for the wake function are

$$f(\eta) = 3\eta^2 - 2\eta^3 \qquad \text{and} \qquad f(\eta) = \sin^2 \left(\tfrac{1}{2}\pi\eta\right),$$

where $\eta = y/\delta$.

To summarise the model for the velocity profile of turbulent flow past a flat plate or in a pipe, we have the following.

(a) *viscous sublayer*:

$$\frac{u}{u_\tau} = \frac{u_\tau y}{\nu} \qquad \left(0 < \frac{u_\tau y}{\nu} < 5\right).$$

Recall that $\delta_\nu = \nu/u_\tau$.

See Equation (4.3).

(b) *buffer layer*: matching function, such as Equation (4.10), for $5 < u_\tau y/\nu < 30$.

(c) *inertial sublayer (overlap layer)*:

$$\frac{u}{u_\tau} = 2.5 \ln \left(\frac{u_\tau y}{\nu}\right) + 5.5 \qquad \left(30 < \frac{u_\tau y}{\nu} < 1000\right)$$

$$= 5.75 \log_{10} \left(\frac{u_\tau y}{\nu}\right) + 5.5.$$

See Equation (4.9).

(d) *outer flow region*:

$$\frac{u}{u_\tau} = 2.5 \ln \left(\frac{u_\tau y}{\nu}\right) + 5.5 + P f \left(\frac{y}{\delta}\right) \qquad \left(\frac{u_\tau y}{\nu} > 1000 \text{ and } \frac{y}{\delta} < 1\right),$$

where $f(0) = 0$, $f(1) = 1$, $f'(1) = 0$ and $P = 0$ for pipes, $P = 2.25$ for external plate flow.

The overall profile is shown, not drawn to scale, in Figure 4.3 (overleaf).

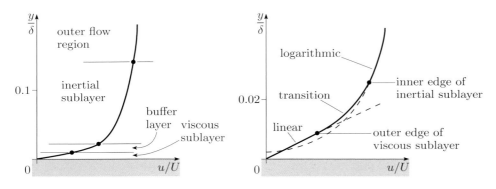

Figure 4.3

This is related to part of Figure 4.2, but with a non-logarithmic distance scale and the axes swapped.

See the *Media Guide* for more on the structure of a turbulent boundary layer.

Exercise 4.4

Water flows within a full pipe of diameter 10 cm at a mean rate (across a cross-section) of $1\,\mathrm{m\,s^{-1}}$. The skin friction coefficient for the flow, $c_f = \tau_0/(\frac{1}{2}\rho U^2)$, has the value 0.0045.

(a) Find the value of the shear stress τ_0 at the wall of the pipe.

(b) Hence find the values of the friction velocity $u_\tau = \sqrt{\tau_0/\rho}$ and viscous length scale $\delta_\nu = \nu/u_\tau$.

(c) Find the distances from the wall of the outside of the laminar sublayer ($5\delta_\nu$) and inside of the inertial sublayer ($30\delta_\nu$).

(d) Use the $\log_{10}$ version of Equation (4.9) to calculate the flow speed u_c at the centre of the pipe.

(e) Find the flow speeds at $y = 30\delta_\nu$ and at $y = 5\delta_\nu$, and express these speeds as percentages of u_c.

For water, take $\rho = 1.0 \times 10^3\,\mathrm{kg\,m^{-3}}$ and $\nu = 1.0 \times 10^{-6}\,\mathrm{m^2\,s^{-1}}$.

You will see in Subsection 4.2 how c_f can be estimated from the Reynolds number of the flow.

Note from the results of Exercise 4.4 how small the thicknesses of the viscous sublayer and buffer layer are: the region in which the logarithmic law applies extends to within about 0.6 mm of the pipe wall (compared with a radius of 5 cm). This illustrates why it is justified for many purposes (one of which you will see in Subsection 4.2) to regard the logarithmic law as applying across the whole pipe.

Note also the very rapid rise in flow speed on moving away from the wall. This speed is already about 56% of its value on the axis of the pipe at 0.6 mm from the wall, which again demonstrates the steep velocity gradient close to the wall and the much flatter gradient further away.

4.2   The friction law for smooth pipes

Here and in the following subsection we concentrate mainly on fully developed turbulent flow within pipes. The aim is to use the logarithmic law (4.9) to express the skin friction coefficient $c_f = \tau_0/(\frac{1}{2}\rho U^2)$, where U is the mean velocity across the pipe, in terms of the Reynolds number Ud/ν, where d is the diameter of the pipe.

However, the results also apply to other fully developed flows, such as open channel flow.

Note first that, since the friction velocity is defined as $u_\tau = \sqrt{\tau_0/\rho}$, we have

$$c_f = \frac{\tau_0}{\frac{1}{2}\rho U^2} = \frac{2u_\tau^2}{U^2}. \tag{4.11}$$

Now since U is the mean velocity across the pipe, the volume flow rate along the pipe is

$$Q = \pi a^2 U, \tag{4.12}$$

where $a = \frac{1}{2}d$ is the radius of the pipe. However, this volume flow rate can also be expressed as an integral across any cross-section S of the pipe, as

$$Q = \int_S u(r)\, dA = \int_{r=0}^{r=a} \int_{\theta=-\pi}^{\theta=\pi} u(r)\, r\, d\theta\, dr$$

$$= 2\pi \int_0^a u(r)\, r\, dr.$$

This integral is given in terms of the radial coordinate r, but in order to use the previously developed expression for the velocity profile, it needs to be expressed in terms of the distance y from the pipe wall, where $y = a - r$. Once this is done, we have

$$Q = 2\pi \int_0^a u(y)\, (a - y)\, dy. \tag{4.13}$$

Assume that the logarithmic law (4.8) or (4.9) applies across the whole cross-section of the pipe, which is justified by the relatively small proportion of the cross-sectional area over which it does not hold, given that the velocity profile is to be integrated across the cross-section. Then from Equations (4.8), (4.12) and (4.13), we obtain

See the comments in the text after Exercise 4.4.

$$\pi a^2 U = 2\pi u_\tau \int_0^a (a - y) \left(A \ln\left(\frac{u_\tau y}{\nu}\right) + B \right) dy,$$

or

There is no need to follow the detail of these manipulations, which lead to Equations (4.14) and (4.15).

$$\frac{U}{u_\tau} = \frac{2}{a^2} \int_0^a (a - y) \left(A \ln\left(\frac{u_\tau y}{\nu}\right) + B \right) dy$$

$$= 2 \int_0^1 (1 - \eta) \left(A \ln\left(\frac{u_\tau a}{\nu}\, \eta\right) + B \right) d\eta, \quad \text{where } \eta = \frac{y}{a},$$

$$= 2 \int_0^1 (1 - \eta) \left(A \ln \eta + C \right) d\eta, \quad \text{where } C = A \ln\left(\frac{u_\tau a}{\nu}\right) + B,$$

$$= \left[\left(1 - (1 - \eta)^2\right) A \ln \eta - 2A\eta + \tfrac{1}{2}A\eta^2 - C(1 - \eta)^2 \right]_0^1$$

$$= -\tfrac{3}{2}A + C = A \ln\left(\frac{u_\tau a}{\nu}\right) + B - \tfrac{3}{2}A.$$

Here integration by parts is required. Note that
$$\lim_{\eta \to 0} (\eta \ln \eta) = 0,$$
so that the integral converges even though the integrand is not bounded at $\eta = 0$.

On inserting the values $A = 2.50$ and $B = 5.5$, as used in Equation (4.9), we have

$$\frac{U}{u_\tau} = 2.50 \ln\left(\frac{u_\tau a}{\nu}\right) + 1.75 = 5.75 \log_{10}\left(\frac{u_\tau a}{\nu}\right) + 1.75. \tag{4.14}$$

Now note that, since $Re = Ud/\nu$,

$$\frac{u_\tau a}{\nu} = \frac{u_\tau}{U} \frac{Ud}{2\nu} = \tfrac{1}{2} Re \frac{u_\tau}{U},$$

where $u_\tau/U = \sqrt{\tfrac{1}{2}c_f}$ from Equation (4.11). We conclude from Equation (4.14) that

$$\sqrt{\frac{2}{c_f}} = 2.50 \ln\left(\tfrac{1}{2} Re \sqrt{\tfrac{1}{2}c_f}\right) + 1.75.$$

On dividing through by $\sqrt{2}$ and writing

$$\ln\left(\tfrac{1}{2}Re\sqrt{\tfrac{1}{2}c_f}\right) = \ln\left(Re\sqrt{c_f}\right) - \ln\left(2\sqrt{2}\right),$$

this becomes

$$\frac{1}{\sqrt{c_f}} \simeq 1.77\ln\left(Re\sqrt{c_f}\right) - 0.60$$

$$\simeq 4.07\log_{10}\left(Re\sqrt{c_f}\right) - 0.60. \tag{4.15}$$

Recall that

$$\ln P - \ln Q = \ln\left(\frac{P}{Q}\right).$$

This equation is the skin friction law that we seek. It is often quoted in terms of the *Darcy friction factor* $\lambda = 4c_f$ rather than in terms of c_f, in which case it takes the form

$$\frac{1}{\sqrt{\lambda}} \simeq 0.884\ln\left(Re\sqrt{\lambda}\right) - 0.91. \tag{4.16}$$

Use of λ rather than c_f is favoured by hydraulic engineers.

However, the numerical values that occur here and in Equation (4.15) are not considered accurate in detail. Just as the constants A and B in Equation (4.8) are assigned slightly different values on the basis of different experiments, this is also true of the constants in Equation (4.16). Experimental results from Prandtl suggested an equation of identical form but with different coefficients, namely,

$$\frac{1}{\sqrt{\lambda}} \simeq 0.869\ln\left(Re\sqrt{\lambda}\right) - 0.80$$

$$\simeq 2.0\log_{10}\left(Re\sqrt{\lambda}\right) - 0.80. \tag{4.17}$$

These can also be written as

$$\frac{1}{\sqrt{\lambda}} \simeq 0.869\ln\left(\frac{Re\sqrt{\lambda}}{2.51}\right)$$

$$\simeq 2.0\log_{10}\left(\frac{Re\sqrt{\lambda}}{2.51}\right).$$

This is known as *Prandtl's universal law of friction for smooth pipes* (abbreviated to the *smooth law*). In terms of the skin friction coefficient, $c_f = \tfrac{1}{4}\lambda$, it becomes

$$\frac{1}{\sqrt{c_f}} \simeq 1.74\ln\left(Re\sqrt{c_f}\right) - 0.40$$

$$\simeq 4.0\log_{10}\left(Re\sqrt{c_f}\right) - 0.40. \tag{4.18}$$

Given a value for Re, Equation (4.17) (or Equation (4.18)) gives a value for λ (or for c_f). However, it only does so *implicitly*, since it is not possible to make λ (or c_f) the subject of the equation.

There are two possible ways to apply Equation (4.17) or (4.18). Solutions for λ or c_f can be tabulated for a range of values of Re, and the results can be displayed graphically. Alternatively, an iterative scheme can be used to generate a solution from an initial trial value. For example, the formula

$$p_{n+1} = [2.0\log_{10}(Re\,p_n) - 0.80]^{-1} \qquad (n=0,1,2,\ldots) \tag{4.19}$$

can be used to solve Equation (4.17) for $\lambda = p^2$. Indeed, the graphical approach can be used to obtain a reasonable starting value $p_0 = \sqrt{\lambda_0}$ for this iteration. Figure 4.4 shows the graph of λ against Re corresponding (for $Re > 4000$) to Equation (4.17). The remaining part of the graph is the corresponding result for laminar flow, $\lambda = 64/Re$. Both scales are logarithmic, and so the laminar section of the graph is a straight line (with slope -1 for a logarithmically marked scale). This applies up to about $Re = 2300$. The region $2300 < Re < 4000$ is approximately where the transition between fully laminar and fully turbulent flow occurs.

Since $\lambda = 4c_f$, this is equivalent to $c_f = 16/Re$, as found in Equation (2.31).

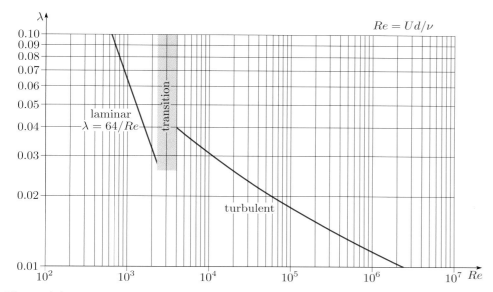

Figure 4.4

Exercise 4.5

Verify that the value $c_f = 0.0045$, given in Exercise 4.4, is appropriate for the situation described there

(a) graphically; (b) by use of the iteration formula (4.19).

For a given volume flow rate along a smooth pipe with known diameter, the Reynolds number can be calculated. Subsequently the skin friction coefficient, c_f, or equivalently the Darcy friction factor, $\lambda = 4c_f$, can be found from Figure 4.4 or from the iteration formula (4.19). Then the Darcy–Weisbach equation,

$$\frac{dp}{dx} = -\frac{2c_f \rho U^2}{d} = -\frac{\lambda \rho U^2}{2d}, \qquad (4.20)$$

which applies to turbulent as well as to laminar flows, can be used to estimate the pressure gradient along the pipe or, equivalently, to find the pressure drop for a given length of pipe.

This summarises the procedure for finding the pressure gradient for a given smooth pipe and flow.

The version for c_f was Equation (2.30).

This procedure also applies, with use of the hydraulic radius R in place of $\frac{1}{4}d$, to other fully developed flows past smooth boundaries, such as flows in part-filled pipes or channels.

Exercise 4.6

A pipe of diameter $20\,\mathrm{cm}$ is to carry water at a volume flow rate of $0.06\,\mathrm{m}^3\,\mathrm{s}^{-1}$ while full. Find the pressure difference along a $10\,\mathrm{m}$ length of the pipe which is required to achieve this.

For water, take $\rho = 1.0 \times 10^3\,\mathrm{kg\,m}^{-3}$ and $\nu = 1.0 \times 10^{-6}\,\mathrm{m}^2\,\mathrm{s}^{-1}$.

A similar analysis to that given for resistance in smooth pipes can be undertaken for external flow over a flat plate, but this presents extra complications and is not included here. The outcome is again an implicit formula for the skin friction coefficient c_f in terms of the Reynolds number. Here $c_f = \tau_0/(\frac{1}{2}\rho U^2)$, where U is the external flow speed, and the Reynolds number is $Re_x = Ux/\nu$. One such formula is

$$\frac{1}{\sqrt{c_f}} \simeq 4.15 \log_{10}\left(Re_x c_f\right) + 1.7.$$

Both Re_x and c_f vary with distance x along the plate. The corresponding graph of c_f against Re_x has the same general features as in Figure 4.4.

4.3   Effect of roughness in pipes

Throughout the discussion in Subsection 4.2, we assumed that the pipes involved were perfectly smooth. In practice, pipes have roughened surfaces, to a greater or lesser extent, and this subsection shows how the roughness of pipe walls affects the skin friction law (4.17) or (4.18).

Figure 4.5 shows what is involved. The roughness of the surface means that the actual boundary for the flow will be uneven, with varying distance away from some baseline chosen for the x-axis and corresponding to a smooth surface. The distance k_s represents the extent to which the rough surface departs from the baseline.

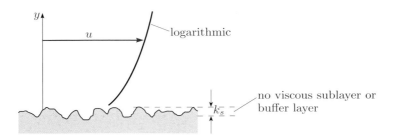

Figure 4.5

This can be put on a more regular footing by imagining the surface to be made up of spheres of diameter k_s, packed tightly above a base plane, as shown in Figure 4.6.

Figure 4.6

This picture approximates the surface of sandpaper; so sand roughness is taken as a standard for measuring roughness in general, and the diameter k_s in Figure 4.6 is called the *sand roughness height*. Other less regular surfaces can then be assigned an *equivalent sand roughness height*.

If k_s is sufficiently large, then, as shown in Figure 4.5, there will be no viscous sublayer or buffer layer in the turbulent flow. The effect of the spheres (in the idealised picture of Figure 4.6) is to shed eddies into the boundary layer, while each sphere can be thought of as having an individual profile drag associated with it. The overall effect, therefore, is to increase the resistance to flow provided by the wall, and hence to increase the pressure gradient that is required to drive flow with a particular volume flow rate.

If k_s is sufficiently small, on the other hand, so that the top of the roughened surface lies within the previously determined viscous sublayer, then the flow will not depart greatly from the pattern described for smooth walls in Subsection 4.1.

An appropriate dimensionless measure of roughness is the ratio $k_s/\delta_\nu = k_s u_\tau/\nu$. The turbulent flow is regarded as *hydraulically smooth* (or just *smooth*) when $k_s u_\tau/\nu < 5$, and in this case the various formulas from Subsections 4.1 and 4.2 still apply, to a good approximation. The flow is called *fully (hydraulically) rough* when $k_s u_\tau/\nu > 70$. In this regime, it turns out that the skin friction coefficient depends on the sand roughness

Some orders of magnitude for equivalent sand roughness height k_s are shown in the table below.

Table 4.1

material	k_s (mm)
'smooth' surface	0.003
PVC pipe	0.05
concrete (spun)	0.15
concrete (rough)	1.5
slimed sewer	3.0
natural river	100

This corresponds to k_s being less than the thickness of the viscous sublayer.

height but is independent of the Reynolds number (unlike the situation in Subsection 4.2). In the region for which $5 < k_s u_\tau/\nu < 70$, there is a transition between smooth and fully rough.

Whatever the size of the sand roughness height, the arguments leading to a logarithmic velocity profile still apply, as indicated in Figure 4.5. As in Subsection 4.1, we arrive at the formula

$$\frac{u}{u_\tau} = \frac{1}{\kappa}\ln y + C, \qquad\qquad (4.6)$$

where $\kappa = 0.40$ and C is a constant. However, when k_s is large, it is no longer appropriate to make the argument of the logarithm dimensionless by writing it as y/δ_ν, since the viscous length scale $\delta_\nu = \nu/u_\tau$ is no longer significant in this situation. An alternative length scale is provided by k_s, and so we can rewrite Equation (4.6) as

$$\frac{u}{u_\tau} = A\ln\left(\frac{y}{k_s}\right) + D, \qquad \text{where } D = C + A\ln k_s. \qquad (4.21)$$

Here $A = 1/\kappa = 2.50$ as before, while the constant D is found experimentally (with $k_s u_\tau/\nu > 70$) to have the value 8.5.

The parameter D in Equation (4.21) is independent of k_s only for large values of $k_s u_\tau/\nu$. More generally, across the full range of possible values for $k_s u_\tau/\nu$, we expect u/u_τ to depend on both k_s and δ_ν. This dependence is best expressed using the dimensionless combination $k_s/\delta_\nu = k_s u_\tau/\nu$. Thus we have

$$\frac{u}{u_\tau} = A\ln\left(\frac{y}{k_s}\right) + h\left(\frac{k_s u_\tau}{\nu}\right), \qquad\qquad (4.22)$$

where $h(k_s u_\tau/\nu) \to 8.5$ for large values of $k_s u_\tau/\nu$. Comparing Equation (4.22) with Equation (4.8), we also require that, for $k_s u_\tau/\nu < 5$,

$$A\ln\left(\frac{u_\tau y}{\nu}\right) + B \simeq A\ln\left(\frac{y}{k_s}\right) + h\left(\frac{k_s u_\tau}{\nu}\right),$$

where $B = 5.5$. Hence, for $k_s u_\tau/\nu < 5$, it follows that

$$h\left(\frac{k_s u_\tau}{\nu}\right) \simeq A\ln\left(\frac{k_s u_\tau}{\nu}\right) + B$$

$$\simeq 2.50\ln\left(\frac{k_s u_\tau}{\nu}\right) + 5.5$$

$$\simeq 5.75\log_{10}\left(\frac{k_s u_\tau}{\nu}\right) + 5.5.$$

The graph of the function h, determined experimentally, is shown in Figure 4.7. It can be seen that this graph matches the behaviour predicted above for $k_s u_\tau/\nu < 5$ and for $k_s u_\tau/\nu > 70$.

Note that $\log_{10} 5 \simeq 0.70$ and $\log_{10} 70 \simeq 1.85$.

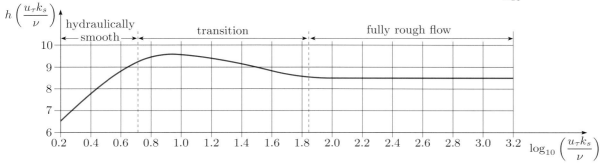

Figure 4.7

113

For $k_s u_\tau / \nu > 70$, Equation (4.22) can be written as

$$\frac{u}{u_\tau} = 2.50 \ln\left(\frac{y}{k_s}\right) + 8.5 = 5.75 \log_{10}\left(\frac{y}{k_s}\right) + 8.5$$

$$= 5.75 \log_{10}\left(\frac{u_\tau y}{\nu}\right) - 5.75 \log_{10}\left(\frac{u_\tau k_s}{\nu}\right) + 8.5. \qquad (4.23)$$

This may also be quoted as

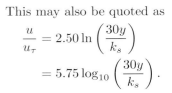

$$\frac{u}{u_\tau} = 2.50 \ln\left(\frac{30y}{k_s}\right)$$
$$= 5.75 \log_{10}\left(\frac{30y}{k_s}\right).$$

This can be compared with Equation (4.9) for the case when $k_s = 0$ (for completely smooth walls), and the graphs of velocity profiles for fully rough flow can be added to that for smooth flow shown in Figure 4.2. The combined picture is shown in Figure 4.8.

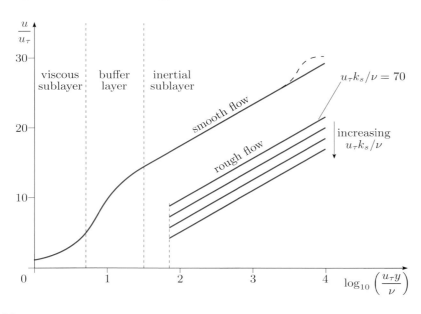

Figure 4.8

A reasonable condition on y for Equation (4.23) to apply is $y > k_s$, since otherwise the roughness elements of the wall extend into the region where the velocity profile is specified.

These results can also be applied to open channel flow, as in the next two exercises.

Exercise 4.7

A wide river has a depth of 5.0 m. Measurements of the flow velocity at 1.0 m and 4.0 m below the water surface give values of $1.2\,\mathrm{m\,s^{-1}}$ and $0.95\,\mathrm{m\,s^{-1}}$, respectively.

Here 'wide' means that the sides of the river can be ignored in the analysis.

(a) Assuming rough turbulent flow, determine the equivalent sand roughness height, k_s, of the river bed. Hence find the friction velocity, u_τ. What is the speed of flow at the surface?

(b) Do your results confirm the assumption of rough flow?

For water, take $\nu = 1.0 \times 10^{-6}\,\mathrm{m^2\,s^{-1}}$.

Exercise 4.8

(a) Integrate Equation (4.21) over the depth h of a wide river, to determine the mean velocity U of the steady flow in terms of h, the roughness size, k_s, and the friction velocity, u_τ.

(b) At what height above the bed, as a fraction of h, is the flow velocity equal to the mean velocity?

(c) Using the result of part (a), and taking $A = 2.50$ and $D = 8.5$ in Equation (4.21), determine the shear stress at the bed in a river flowing with $h = 2.5\,\mathrm{m}$, $U = 1.2\,\mathrm{m\,s^{-1}}$ and $k_s = 0.2\,\mathrm{m}$.

For water, take $\rho = 1.0 \times 10^3\,\mathrm{kg\,m^{-3}}$.

We have now specified u/u_τ for $k_s = 0$ (Equation (4.9)) and for $k_s u_\tau/\nu > 70$ (Equation (4.23)). The question remains of how the velocity profile behaves for values of $k_s u_\tau/\nu < 70$. One approach is to specify a function which has the correct limiting behaviour for $k_s = 0$ and for large k_s; one possibility is

$$\frac{u}{u_\tau} = -2.50\ln\left(\frac{3.32\nu}{u_\tau y} + \frac{k_s}{y}\right) + 8.5, \qquad (4.24)$$

Note that
$$-\ln\left(\frac{P}{Q}\right) = \ln\left(\frac{Q}{P}\right).$$

which turns out to give a reasonable match with experimental results. When k_s is large, the first term in the brackets is relatively insignificant, and we have Equation (4.23). On the other hand, when $k_s = 0$ we have Equation (4.9), since

$$-2.50\ln(3.32) + 8.5 \simeq 5.5.$$

Now Equation (4.24) is of the same functional form (for y) as Equation (4.8), with $A = 2.50$ as before, $B = 8.5$ (instead of 5.5) and $3.32\nu/u_\tau + k_s$ in place of ν/u_τ. Hence the argument of Subsection 4.2 (leading there to Equation (4.14)) can be followed through as before, to reach

$$\frac{U}{u_\tau} = A\ln\left(\frac{a}{3.32\nu/u_\tau + k_s}\right) + B - \tfrac{3}{2}A$$

Here U is the mean velocity across a cross-section and $Re = Ud/\nu$.

$$= -2.50\ln\left(\frac{3.32\nu}{u_\tau a} + \frac{k_s}{a}\right) + 4.75.$$

As before, $a = \tfrac{1}{2}d$ and

$$\frac{u_\tau a}{\nu} = \tfrac{1}{2}Re\,\frac{u_\tau}{U}, \qquad \frac{u_\tau}{U} = \sqrt{\tfrac{1}{2}c_f},$$

so that

$$\sqrt{\frac{2}{c_f}} = -2.50\ln\left(\frac{6.64}{Re}\sqrt{\frac{2}{c_f}} + \frac{2k_s}{d}\right) + 4.75, \qquad \text{or}$$

$$\frac{1}{\sqrt{c_f}} = -1.768\ln\left(\frac{9.39}{Re\sqrt{c_f}} + \frac{2k_s}{d}\right) + 3.36.$$

In terms of the Darcy friction factor, $\lambda = 4c_f$, this reads as

$$\frac{1}{\sqrt{\lambda}} = -0.884\ln\left(\frac{18.8}{Re\sqrt{\lambda}} + \frac{2k_s}{d}\right) + 1.68.$$

As with Equation (4.17) for smooth pipes, experiments confirm the form of this equation but point to slightly different values for the coefficients, namely,

$$\frac{1}{\sqrt{\lambda}} = -0.869 \ln \left(\frac{18.6}{Re\sqrt{\lambda}} + \frac{2k_s}{d} \right) + 1.74.$$

By 'taking the 1.74 inside the logarithm', this can also be written as

$$\frac{1}{\sqrt{\lambda}} = -0.869 \ln \left(\frac{2.51}{Re\sqrt{\lambda}} + \frac{k_s}{3.70d} \right)$$

$$= -2.0 \log_{10} \left(\frac{2.51}{Re\sqrt{\lambda}} + \frac{k_s}{3.70d} \right). \qquad (4.25)$$

This is known as the *Colebrook–White equation*. When $k_s = 0$, it reduces to the smooth law (4.17). In general, it gives the Darcy friction factor λ implicitly as a function of the two parameters Re and k_s/d. However, for fully rough flow, where the first term in the bracket is negligible, it gives the *explicit* formula

This also arises in the limit as $Re \to \infty$.

$$\frac{1}{\sqrt{\lambda}} = -2.0 \log_{10} \left(\frac{k_s}{3.70d} \right). \qquad (4.26)$$

This can be applied whenever $k_s u_\tau/\nu > 70$.

As it stands, the Colebrook–White equation (4.25) applies to full pipes, but it can be extended to pipes running part-full or to open channel flows by employing the hydraulic radius, R, introduced in Subsection 2.5. Putting $4R$ in place of d in Equation (4.25) gives

Recall that for a pipe, the hydraulic radius is half of the actual radius.

$$\frac{1}{\sqrt{\lambda}} = -2.0 \log_{10} \left(\frac{2.51\nu}{4UR\sqrt{\lambda}} + \frac{k_s}{14.8R} \right). \qquad (4.27)$$

As with the smooth law (4.17), it is possible to solve Equation (4.25) or (4.27) iteratively; one possible formula for doing so is

$$p_{n+1} = -\frac{1}{2} \left[\log_{10} \left(\frac{2.51}{Re\, p_n} + \frac{k_s}{3.70d} \right) \right]^{-1} \qquad (n = 0, 1, 2, \ldots), \qquad (4.28)$$

where $\lambda = p^2$. Here too there is a graphical alternative, which can be used to obtain a starting value for Equation (4.28) if more precision is required. The *Moody diagram* shown in Figure 4.9 provides this information. This is based on the corresponding diagram for smooth pipes, Figure 4.4, but includes further curves for a range of values of the dimensionless roughness parameter k_s/d (shown at the right of the diagram).

For a given volume flow rate along a pipe with known diameter, d, and equivalent sand roughness height, k_s, the Reynolds number and parameter k_s/d can be calculated. Subsequently, the skin friction coefficient, c_f, or equivalently the Darcy friction factor, $\lambda = 4c_f$, can be found from the Moody diagram or from the iteration formula (4.28). Then the Darcy–Weisbach equation (4.20) can be used to estimate the pressure gradient along the pipe or, equivalently, to find the pressure drop for a given length of pipe. This procedure is very similar to the one for smooth pipes described in the text after Exercise 4.5.

This summarises the procedure for finding the pressure gradient for a given rough pipe and flow.

A similar analysis can be undertaken for external flow past a rough plate, but that is not included here.

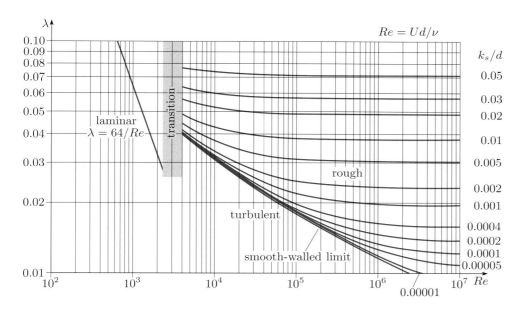

Figure 4.9   Moody diagram

Exercise 4.9

Use the Colebrook–White equation (4.25) to find the Darcy friction factor for a pipe with diameter 25 cm and equivalent sand roughness height 0.25 mm, when the volume flow rate of water in a full pipe is $0.157\,\mathrm{m^3\,s^{-1}}$.

For water, take $\nu = 1.0 \times 10^{-6}\,\mathrm{m^2\,s^{-1}}$.

End-of-section exercise

Exercise 4.10

(a) A pipe of diameter 25 cm, running full, discharges water at a mean velocity of $8.0\,\mathrm{m\,s^{-1}}$. If the equivalent sand roughness height of the pipe wall is $k_s = 0.25$ mm, and the Darcy friction factor is $\lambda = 0.020$, find the shear stress at the wall and the friction velocity.

For water, take $\rho = 1.0 \times 10^3\,\mathrm{kg\,m^{-3}}$ and $\nu = 1.0 \times 10^{-6}\,\mathrm{m^2\,s^{-1}}$.

(b) Check that the flow is turbulent and rough. If u_c is the flow velocity on the axis of the pipe (and hence the maximum velocity), find u/u_c as a function of y/a, where a is the radius of the pipe. Plot this velocity profile on a graph, and compare it with the profile given by the one-seventh power law.

(c) If the volume flow rate is now reduced by a factor of 100, find the new Darcy friction factor, shear stress at the wall and friction velocity. Plot the new velocity profile and compare it with the previous case.

(d) If the volume flow rate is now reduced by a further factor of 20, show that the flow is laminar. Find the new Darcy friction factor and shear stress at the wall. Plot the new velocity profile and compare it with the previous cases.

117

Outcomes

After studying this unit you should be able to:

- explain how a boundary layer of a viscous flow allows an inviscid exterior flow to be matched with the no-slip condition at the boundary;

- describe the main features of turbulent flow, how it differs from laminar flow, and how transition occurs;

- follow the development of the laminar boundary layer equations, and appreciate that the momentum integral equation is a consequence;

- apply the momentum integral equation for zero external pressure gradient to a trial velocity profile, to find the displacement thickness, momentum thickness, skin friction coefficient, shear stress and total skin friction drag force on a flat plate;

- appreciate that the Blasius equation leads to an exact solution of the boundary layer equations, and describe the features of this solution;

- derive the Darcy–Weisbach equation for either laminar or turbulent flow in a pipe, and apply this equation to obtain a pressure gradient or pressure drop for a given pipe, flow and friction factor;

- apply the momentum integral equation for turbulent flow, given a trial mean velocity profile ($1/n$ power law) and corresponding boundary shear stress distribution, to find the skin friction drag force on a plate;

- appreciate the role of the kinematic eddy viscosity and mixing length in modelling the Reynolds stresses;

- describe the layered structure of the mean velocity profile within a turbulent boundary layer;

- appreciate how the model of turbulent flow in pipes can be amended to take the roughness of pipes into account;

- apply the friction law for turbulent flow in rough or smooth pipes, to find the Darcy friction factor or skin friction coefficient, either from the Moody diagram or by using an iteration formula.

Acknowledgements

The Course Team acknowledges the very significant part played in the creation of *Unit 13* by Donald Knight, Emeritus Professor of Water Engineering at the University of Birmingham.

Grateful acknowledgement is also made to the following sources:

Figure 1.5: 'Klebanoff's data for boundary layer flow', Schlichting, H. (1979), *Boundary Layer Theory*, McGraw-Hill;

Figure 1.7: Reynolds, O. (1883), 'An experimental investigation', Plate 73, *Philosophical Transactions of the Royal Society of London*, 1 January, vol. 174, pp. 935–982;

Figures 1.13, 1.14 and 2.9: Schlichting, H. and Gersten, K. (2000), *Boundary Layer Theory*, Springer;

Figures 4.2 and 4.7: Duncan, W.J., Thom, A.S. and Young, A.D. (1970), *Mechanics of Fluids*, Edward Arnold.

Every effort has been made to contact copyright holders. If any have been inadvertently overlooked the publishers will be pleased to make the necessary arrangements at the first opportunity.

Solutions to the exercises

Section 1

Solution 1.1

(a) With $U = 0.5\,\mathrm{m\,s^{-1}}$, $d = 0.012\,\mathrm{m}$ and $\nu = 1.0 \times 10^{-6}\,\mathrm{m^2\,s^{-1}}$, we have
$$Re = \frac{Ud}{\nu} = \frac{0.5 \times 0.012}{1.0 \times 10^{-6}} = 6000.$$

(b) Since $Re > 2300$ in part (a), the flow is turbulent. For laminar flow, we require $Re < 2300$, or
$$0.012U \times 10^6 < 2300, \qquad \text{giving} \qquad U < 0.19\,\mathrm{m\,s^{-1}}.$$

Solution 1.2

For a volume flow rate V, the mean velocity is $U = 4V/(\pi d^2)$, giving the Reynolds number
$$Re = \frac{Ud}{\nu} = \frac{4V \times 0.005}{\pi (0.005)^2 \nu} = \frac{800V}{\pi \nu}.$$
Now take $Re = 2300$, to obtain $V = \frac{23}{8}\pi\nu$.

(a) For water, with $\nu = 1.0 \times 10^{-6}\,\mathrm{m^2\,s^{-1}}$, we have
$$V = \tfrac{23}{8}\pi \times 10^{-6} \simeq 9.0 \times 10^{-6}\,\mathrm{m^3\,s^{-1}}$$
$$= 9.0 \times 10^{-3}\,\mathrm{l\,s^{-1}}.$$

(b) For air, with $\nu = 1.5 \times 10^{-5}\,\mathrm{m^2\,s^{-1}}$, we obtain
$$V = \tfrac{23}{8}\pi \times 1.5 \times 10^{-5} \simeq 1.4 \times 10^{-4}\,\mathrm{m^3\,s^{-1}}$$
$$= 0.14\,\mathrm{l\,s^{-1}}.$$

Section 2

Solution 2.1

(a) Since $u(x,0) = 0$ and $v(x,0) = 0$, it follows that
$$\frac{\partial u}{\partial x}(x,0) = 0 \qquad \text{and} \qquad \frac{\partial v}{\partial x}(x,0) = 0.$$
Applying the continuity equation (2.1) at $y = 0$ gives
$$\frac{\partial u}{\partial x}(x,0) + \frac{\partial v}{\partial y}(x,0) = 0.$$
However, the first term is zero, from above, and so
$$\frac{\partial v}{\partial y}(x,0) = 0.$$

(b) Since $u(x,0) = v(x,0) = 0$, the result
$$-U\frac{dU}{dx} = \nu\left[\frac{\partial^2 u}{\partial y^2}\right]_{y=0} = \frac{1}{\rho}\left[\frac{\partial \tau}{\partial y}\right]_{y=0}$$
follows directly from Equation (2.9) and the given definition of shear stress.

Solution 2.2

We simplify the integrals as in Example 2.1(c). From Equation (2.14), the displacement thickness δ_1 is given by
$$\frac{\delta_1}{\delta} = \int_0^1 \left(1 - \frac{u}{U}\right) d\eta = \int_0^1 (1 - \eta)\,d\eta$$
$$= \left[\eta - \tfrac{1}{2}\eta^2\right]_0^1 = \tfrac{1}{2},$$
so that $\delta_1 = \tfrac{1}{2}\delta$. Similarly, from Equation (2.15), the momentum thickness δ_2 is given by
$$\frac{\delta_2}{\delta} = \int_0^1 \frac{u}{U}\left(1 - \frac{u}{U}\right) d\eta = \int_0^1 \eta(1 - \eta)\,d\eta$$
$$= \int_0^1 (\eta - \eta^2)\,d\eta$$
$$= \left[\tfrac{1}{2}\eta^2 - \tfrac{1}{3}\eta^3\right]_0^1 = \tfrac{1}{6},$$
so that $\delta_2 = \tfrac{1}{6}\delta$. Also
$$\tau_0 = \mu\left[\frac{\partial u}{\partial y}\right]_{y=0} = \frac{\mu U}{\delta}.$$
The momentum integral equation (2.16) then gives
$$\frac{1}{6}\frac{d\delta}{dx} = \frac{\mu U}{\rho U^2 \delta}, \qquad \text{or} \qquad \frac{d(\delta^2)}{dx} = \frac{12\nu}{U}.$$
Integration, with $\delta = 0$ when $x = 0$, gives
$$\delta = 3.464\left(\frac{\nu x}{U}\right)^{1/2} \qquad \text{or} \qquad \frac{\delta}{x} = 3.464(Re_x)^{-1/2}.$$
It follows that
$$\tau_0 = \frac{\mu U}{\delta} = \frac{\mu U}{\sqrt{12}}\left(\frac{U}{\nu x}\right)^{1/2} = 0.289\left(\frac{\mu\rho U^3}{x}\right)^{1/2},$$
and
$$c_f = \frac{\tau_0}{\frac{1}{2}\rho U^2} = 0.577(Re_x)^{-1/2}.$$
The total skin friction drag force is
$$F_L = \int_0^L \tau_0\,dx = 0.577(\mu\rho U^3 L)^{1/2}.$$
Hence
$$K_1 = 3.464, \quad K_2 = 0.577, \quad K_3 = 0.500, \quad K_4 = 3.00.$$

Solution 2.3

For
$$f(\eta) = 2\eta - 2\eta^3 + \eta^4, \qquad \text{where } \eta = y/\delta,$$
we have
$$f(0) = f(1) - 1 = 0,$$
$$f'(1) = \left[2 - 6\eta^2 + 4\eta^3\right]_{\eta=1} = 0,$$
$$f''(0) = \left[-12\eta + 12\eta^2\right]_{\eta=0} = 0 \quad \text{and} \quad f''(1) = 0.$$
Since $u = U f(y/\delta)$ and
$$\frac{\partial u}{\partial y} = \frac{U}{\delta}f'\left(\frac{y}{\delta}\right), \qquad \frac{\partial^2 u}{\partial y^2} = \frac{U}{\delta^2}f''\left(\frac{y}{\delta}\right),$$
the given profile satisfies all five of the conditions (2.19).

Solution 2.4

Since $\tau_0 \propto x^{-1/2}$, the shear stress on the plate is greater when closer to the leading edge. Hence the total skin friction drag will be greater when the shorter side is parallel to the flow.

The total drag on a plate of length L and breadth B is

$$BF_L = B \int_0^L \tau_0 \, dx,$$

where F_L is the drag force per unit breadth for length L. Now

$$\tau_0 = \tfrac{1}{2}\rho U^2 c_f = \tfrac{1}{2}\rho U^2 K_2 (Re_x)^{-1/2},$$

where $Re_x = Ux/\nu$, so that

$$BF_L = \tfrac{1}{2}K_2 \rho U^{3/2} \nu^{1/2} B \int_0^L x^{-1/2} \, dx$$

$$= K_2 \rho U^{3/2} \nu^{1/2} B L^{1/2}.$$

Hence

$$\frac{4pF_p}{pF_{4p}} = \frac{4p \times p^{1/2}}{p \times (4p)^{1/2}} = 2;$$

so the drag force with the shorter side parallel to the flow is twice that with the longer side parallel to the flow.

(Note that this result is independent of which velocity profile is chosen from Table 2.2, since it depends only on the fact that $\tau_0 \propto x^{-1/2}$ and hence that $F_L \propto L^{1/2}$.)

Solution 2.5

From Solution 2.4, the total skin friction drag per unit breadth is

$$F_L = K_2 \rho U^{3/2} \nu^{1/2} L^{1/2}.$$

In this case, $K_2 = 0.664$, $\rho = 1.0 \times 10^3 \, \text{kg m}^{-3}$, $\nu = \mu/\rho = 1.0 \times 10^{-6} \, \text{m}^2\,\text{s}^{-1}$, $U = 1\,\text{m s}^{-1}$ and $L = 0.3\,\text{m}$. Hence

$$F_L = 0.664 \times 10^3 \times 1^{3/2} \times 10^{-3} \times (0.3)^{1/2}$$

$$\simeq 0.364 \, \text{N m}^{-1}.$$

Solution 2.6

Since the volume flow rate is constant, while the flow towards the wall of the pipe is increasingly retarded by the growing boundary layer, the inviscid flow in the region external to the boundary layer must speed up to compensate. This will apply in particular along the axis of the pipe. According to Bernoulli's equation, the pressure therefore decreases along this line.

Solution 2.7

Since $\tau = -\mu \, \partial u/\partial r$, the shear stress in the pipe is

$$\tau = -\mu \frac{d}{dr}\left(\frac{C}{4\mu}\left(a^2 - r^2\right)\right) = \tfrac{1}{2}Cr.$$

Thus τ varies linearly with radial distance across the pipe. Its value at the pipe wall ($r = a$) is

$$\tau_0 = \tfrac{1}{2}Ca = -\tfrac{1}{2}a\frac{dp}{dx}.$$

Solution 2.8

(a) The shear stress is given by

$$\tau(y) = \mu \frac{\partial u}{\partial y} = \frac{\mu C(h - 2y)}{2\mu}; \qquad \text{so}$$

$$\tau_0 = \tau(0) = \tfrac{1}{2}Ch.$$

(b) The mean flow speed, U, is given by

$$U = \frac{1}{h}\int_0^h u \, dy = \frac{C}{2\mu h}\int_0^h (yh - y^2) \, dy$$

$$= \frac{C}{2\mu h}\left[\tfrac{1}{2}hy^2 - \tfrac{1}{3}y^3\right]_0^h = \frac{Ch^2}{12\mu}.$$

(c) From parts (a) and (b), the skin friction coefficient c_f is

$$c_f = \frac{\tau_0}{\tfrac{1}{2}\rho U^2} = \frac{2\tau_0}{\rho U} \times \frac{1}{U} = \frac{Ch}{\rho U} \times \frac{12\mu}{Ch^2} = \frac{12}{Re},$$

where $Re = \rho U h/\mu = U h/\nu$.

(d) Since $dp/dx = -C = -2\tau_0/h$, we have

$$\frac{dp}{dx} = -\frac{2}{h} \times \tfrac{1}{2}\rho U^2 c_f = -\frac{\rho c_f}{h}U^2,$$

which is the analogue of the Darcy–Weisbach equation (2.30) in this case.

Solution 2.9

(a) With

$$\frac{u}{U} = f\left(\frac{y}{\delta}\right) = \frac{3}{2}\left(\frac{y}{\delta}\right) - \frac{1}{2}\left(\frac{y}{\delta}\right)^3, \qquad \text{or}$$

$$f(\eta) = \tfrac{3}{2}\eta - \tfrac{1}{2}\eta^3, \qquad \text{where } \eta = y/\delta,$$

we have

$$f(0) = f(1) - 1 = 0,$$

$$f'(1) = \left[\tfrac{3}{2} - \tfrac{3}{2}\eta^2\right]_{\eta=1} = 0,$$

$$f''(0) = [-3\eta]_{\eta=0} = 0 \quad \text{but} \quad f''(1) \neq 0.$$

Hence (reasoning as in Solution 2.3) the profile satisfies all of the conditions (2.19) except for $(\partial^2 u/\partial y^2)(x, \delta) = 0$.

(b) We proceed as in Example 2.1(c) and (d). From Equation (2.14), the displacement thickness δ_1 is given by

$$\frac{\delta_1}{\delta} = \int_0^1 \left(1 - \frac{u}{U}\right) d\eta = \int_0^1 \left(1 - \tfrac{3}{2}\eta + \tfrac{1}{2}\eta^3\right) d\eta$$

$$= \left[\eta - \tfrac{3}{4}\eta^2 + \tfrac{1}{8}\eta^4\right]_0^1 = \tfrac{3}{8},$$

so that $\delta_1 = \tfrac{3}{8}\delta$. Similarly, from Equation (2.15), the momentum thickness δ_2 is given by

$$\frac{\delta_2}{\delta} = \int_0^1 \frac{u}{U}\left(1 - \frac{u}{U}\right) d\eta$$

$$= \int_0^1 \left(\tfrac{3}{2}\eta - \tfrac{1}{2}\eta^3\right)\left(1 - \tfrac{3}{2}\eta + \tfrac{1}{2}\eta^3\right) d\eta$$

$$= \int_0^1 \left(\tfrac{3}{2}\eta - \tfrac{9}{4}\eta^2 - \tfrac{1}{2}\eta^3 + \tfrac{3}{2}\eta^4 - \tfrac{1}{4}\eta^6\right) d\eta$$

$$= \left[\tfrac{3}{4}\eta^2 - \tfrac{3}{4}\eta^3 - \tfrac{1}{8}\eta^4 + \tfrac{3}{10}\eta^5 - \tfrac{1}{28}\eta^7\right]_0^1 = \tfrac{39}{280},$$

so that $\delta_2 = \tfrac{39}{280}\delta$. Also

$$\tau_0 = \mu \left[\frac{\partial u}{\partial y}\right]_{y=0} = \frac{3\mu U}{2\delta}.$$

The momentum integral equation (2.16) then gives

$$\frac{39}{280}\frac{d\delta}{dx} = \frac{3\mu U}{2\rho U^2 \delta}, \qquad \text{or} \qquad \frac{d(\delta^2)}{dx} = \frac{280\nu}{13U}.$$

Integration, with $\delta = 0$ when $x = 0$, gives

$$\delta = 4.641\left(\frac{\nu x}{U}\right)^{1/2} \qquad \text{or} \qquad \frac{\delta}{x} = 4.641(Re_x)^{-1/2}.$$

It follows that

$$\tau_0 = \frac{3\mu U}{2\delta} = \frac{3\mu U}{2}\sqrt{\frac{13}{280}}\left(\frac{U}{\nu x}\right)^{1/2} = 0.323\left(\frac{\mu\rho U^3}{x}\right)^{1/2},$$

and

$$c_f = \frac{\tau_0}{\frac{1}{2}\rho U^2} = 0.646(Re_x)^{-1/2}.$$

The total skin friction drag force is

$$F_L = \int_0^L \tau_0\,dx = 0.646(\mu\rho U^3 L)^{1/2}.$$

Hence

$$K_1 = 4.641, \quad K_2 = 0.646, \quad K_3 = 0.375, \quad K_4 = 2.69.$$

(An alternative way of finding c_f is to note that $\delta_2 = kx^{1/2}$ (k constant), so that

$$\frac{d\delta_2}{dx} = \tfrac{1}{2}kx^{-1/2} = \frac{\delta_2}{2x}, \quad \text{and} \quad c_f = 2\frac{d\delta_2}{dx} = \frac{\delta_2}{x}.$$

This applies to all of the velocity profiles considered in Subsection 2.2.)

Section 3

Solution 3.1

(a) With $\tau_{xx} = 2\mu\,\partial u/\partial x$, $\tau_{yy} = 2\mu\,\partial v/\partial y$, $\tau_{zz} = 2\mu\,\partial w/\partial z$, the left-hand side of Equation (3.4) becomes

$$\tau_{xx} + \tau_{yy} + \tau_{zz} = 2\mu\left(\frac{\partial u}{\partial x} + \frac{\partial v}{\partial y} + \frac{\partial w}{\partial z}\right)$$
$$= 2\mu\,\mathrm{div}\,\mathbf{u} = 0,$$

from the continuity equation for an incompressible fluid. Hence Equation (3.4) is satisfied.

(b) The x-component of Cauchy's equation (3.7) is

$$\rho\frac{du}{dt} = -\frac{\partial p}{\partial x} + \rho F_x + \frac{\partial}{\partial x}(\tau_{xx}) + \frac{\partial}{\partial y}(\tau_{xy}) + \frac{\partial}{\partial z}(\tau_{xz}).$$

From the specification (3.8), the last three terms become

$$2\mu\frac{\partial}{\partial x}\left(\frac{\partial u}{\partial x}\right) + \mu\frac{\partial}{\partial y}\left(\frac{\partial v}{\partial x} + \frac{\partial u}{\partial y}\right) + \mu\frac{\partial}{\partial z}\left(\frac{\partial w}{\partial x} + \frac{\partial u}{\partial z}\right)$$
$$= \mu\left(\frac{\partial^2 u}{\partial x^2} + \frac{\partial^2 u}{\partial y^2} + \frac{\partial^2 u}{\partial z^2}\right) + \mu\left(\frac{\partial^2 u}{\partial x^2} + \frac{\partial^2 v}{\partial x\,\partial y} + \frac{\partial^2 w}{\partial x\,\partial z}\right)$$
$$= \mu\nabla^2 u + \mu\frac{\partial}{\partial x}\left(\frac{\partial u}{\partial x} + \frac{\partial v}{\partial y} + \frac{\partial w}{\partial z}\right)$$
$$= \mu\nabla^2 u, \qquad \text{from the continuity equation.}$$

The result for the x-component of the Navier–Stokes equation (3.9) follows, and the argument for the other two components is similar.

Solution 3.2

The dimensions of shear stress (force per unit area) are $(\mathrm{M\,L\,T^{-2}})\,\mathrm{L^{-2}} = \mathrm{M\,L^{-1}\,T^{-2}}$.

Each of u', v', w' are velocities, and the time-averaging process has no effect on dimensions. Hence the expressions for the Reynolds stresses have the dimensions of density $\times$ (velocity)^2, that is,

$$(\mathrm{M\,L^{-3}})(\mathrm{L\,T^{-1}})^2 = \mathrm{M\,L^{-1}\,T^{-2}},$$

which are the same as for shear stress.

Solution 3.3

(a) Using the approach of Example 2.1(c), and writing $\eta = y/\delta$, the displacement thickness is

$$\delta_1 = \delta\int_0^1\left(1 - \eta^{1/7}\right)d\eta$$
$$= \delta\left[\eta - \tfrac{7}{8}\eta^{8/7}\right]_0^1 = \tfrac{1}{8}\delta.$$

Similarly, the momentum thickness is

$$\delta_2 = \delta\int_0^1\eta^{1/7}\left(1 - \eta^{1/7}\right)d\eta = \delta\int_0^1\left(\eta^{1/7} - \eta^{2/7}\right)d\eta$$
$$= \delta\left[\tfrac{7}{8}\eta^{8/7} - \tfrac{7}{9}\eta^{9/7}\right]_0^1 = \left(\tfrac{7}{8} - \tfrac{7}{9}\right)\delta = \tfrac{7}{72}\delta.$$

(b) The momentum integral equation (3.24) gives

$$\frac{7}{72}\frac{d\delta}{dx} = \frac{\tau_0}{\rho U^2} = \frac{0.0225}{(U\delta/\nu)^{1/4}}, \qquad \text{or}$$

$$\delta^{1/4}\frac{d\delta}{dx} = \frac{72}{7}\times\frac{0.0225}{(U/\nu)^{1/4}}.$$

Integration gives (since $\delta = 0$ when $x = 0$)

$$\tfrac{4}{5}\delta^{5/4} = \frac{72}{7}\times\frac{0.0225x}{(U/\nu)^{1/4}}, \qquad \text{or}$$

$$\delta = \left(\frac{5}{4}\times\frac{72}{7}\times\frac{0.0225x}{(U/\nu)^{1/4}}\right)^{4/5}, \qquad \text{that is,}$$

$$\frac{\delta}{x} = \frac{0.371}{(Ux/\nu)^{1/5}}.$$

Hence

$$\tau_0 = \frac{0.0225\rho U^2}{(U\delta/\nu)^{1/4}} = \frac{0.0225\rho U^2}{(U/\nu)^{1/4}}\left(\frac{0.371x}{(Ux/\nu)^{1/5}}\right)^{-1/4}$$
$$= \frac{0.0288\rho U^2}{(Ux/\nu)^{1/5}}.$$

The total skin friction drag per unit breadth on a plate of length L is given by

$$F_L = \int_0^L \tau_0\,dx = \frac{0.0288\rho U^2}{(U/\nu)^{1/5}}\int_0^L x^{-1/5}\,dx$$
$$= \frac{0.0288\rho U^2}{(U/\nu)^{1/5}}\times\tfrac{5}{4}L^{4/5} = \frac{0.0360\rho U^2 L}{(UL/\nu)^{1/5}}.$$

Solution 3.4

(a) The mean flow velocity is

$$U = \frac{1.6}{2.0\times 0.4} = 2\,\mathrm{m\,s^{-1}},$$

which may be taken as the flow rate external to the boundary layer. The Reynolds number Ux/ν at the end of the channel is

$$\frac{Ux}{\nu} = \frac{2\times 8}{1\times 10^{-6}} = 1.6\times 10^7.$$

From Solution 3.3(b), the boundary layer thickness at $x = 8$ is

$$\delta = \frac{0.371x}{(Ux/\nu)^{1/5}} = \frac{0.371 \times 8.0}{(1.6 \times 10^7)^{1/5}} \simeq 0.108\,\text{m},$$

so that (from Solution 3.3(a)) the corresponding displacement thickness is

$$\delta_1 = \tfrac{1}{8}\delta = 0.0134\,\text{m}.$$

(b) For a water cross-section of breadth b and height h, the total area is

$$bh = 2.0 \times 0.4 = 0.8\,\text{m}^2,$$

while the effective area at the end of the channel is

$$(b - 2\delta_1)(h - \delta_1) \simeq 0.763\,\text{m}^2.$$

The reduction in effective cross-sectional area is therefore

$$\frac{0.8 - 0.763}{0.8} \simeq 4.7\%.$$

Solution 3.5

(a) If

$$\tau_0 = 0.332\rho U^2 (Re_x)^{-1/2} = 0.0288\rho U^2 (Re_x)^{-1/5},$$

then

$$\frac{0.332}{0.0288} = (Re_x)^{1/2 - 1/5} = (Re_x)^{3/10},$$

so that

$$Re_x = \left(\frac{0.332}{0.0288}\right)^{10/3} \simeq 3460.$$

(b) If

$$F_L = 0.664\rho U^2 L (Re_L)^{-1/2} = 0.0360\rho U^2 L (Re_L)^{-1/5},$$

then

$$\frac{0.664}{0.0360} = (Re_L)^{3/10},$$

so that

$$Re_L = \left(\frac{0.664}{0.0360}\right)^{10/3} \simeq 16\,600.$$

Solution 3.6

Since $\tau_0 \propto x^{-1/5}$, the shear stress on the plate is greater when closer to the leading edge. Hence the total skin friction drag will be greater when the shorter side is parallel to the flow.

The total drag on a plate of length L and breadth B, from Table 3.1, is

$$BF_L = \frac{0.0360\rho U^2 BL}{(UL/\nu)^{1/5}}$$
$$= 0.0360\rho U^{9/5}\nu^{1/5}BL^{4/5}.$$

Hence

$$\frac{4pF_p}{pF_{4p}} = \frac{4p \times p^{4/5}}{p \times (4p)^{4/5}} = 4^{1/5} \simeq 1.32;$$

so the drag force with the shorter side parallel to the flow is about 1.3 times that with the longer side parallel to the flow. (This ratio is less than the corresponding answer for laminar flow in Solution 2.4.)

Solution 3.7

(a) With $\nu = \mu/\rho = 1.5 \times 10^{-5}\,\text{m}^2\,\text{s}^{-1}$, the Reynolds number is

$$Re_L = \frac{UL}{\nu} = \frac{56 \times 210}{1.5 \times 10^{-5}} = 7.84 \times 10^8,$$

and so from Table 3.1 the total skin friction drag force for breadth $10.75\,\text{m}$ is

$$10.75F_{210} = \frac{10.75 \times 0.0360 \times 1.20 \times 56^2 \times 210}{(7.84 \times 10^8)^{1/5}}$$
$$\simeq 5.09 \times 10^3\,\text{N}.$$

Multiplying this by the speed $56\,\text{m s}^{-1}$ gives the power required to overcome skin friction as $285\,\text{kW}$. (Further power will be needed to overcome the profile drag.)

(b) Since the boundary layer becomes thicker along the train, its maximum thickness is at the back end, where

$$\delta(L) = 0.371L(Re_L)^{-1/5}$$
$$= 0.371 \times 210 \times (7.84 \times 10^8)^{-1/5} \simeq 1.30\,\text{m}.$$

(This is a similar distance to that at which yellow lines are drawn on UK railway platforms, to warn passengers not to approach the edge of the platform too closely.)

(c) For a hypothetical laminar flow, the corresponding values (from Table 3.1) would be

$$10.75F_{210} = \frac{10.75 \times 0.664 \times 1.20 \times 56^2 \times 210}{(7.84 \times 10^8)^{1/2}}$$
$$\simeq 201\,\text{N},$$

requiring power at a rate of $11.3\,\text{kW}$, and

$$\delta = 5 \times 210 \times (7.84 \times 10^8)^{-1/2}$$
$$\simeq 0.0375\,\text{m} = 3.75\,\text{cm}.$$

The (real) turbulent flow produces a drag force 25 times greater than the hypothetical laminar flow, with a maximum boundary layer thickness 35 times greater.

Solution 3.8

(a) Using the approach of Example 2.1(c), and writing $\eta = y/\delta$, the displacement thickness is

$$\delta_1 = \delta \int_0^1 \left(1 - \eta^{1/9}\right) d\eta$$
$$= \delta \left[\eta - \tfrac{9}{10}\eta^{10/9}\right]_0^1 = \tfrac{1}{10}\delta.$$

Similarly, the momentum thickness is

$$\delta_2 = \delta \int_0^1 \eta^{1/9}\left(1 - \eta^{1/9}\right) d\eta = \delta \int_0^1 \left(\eta^{1/9} - \eta^{2/9}\right) d\eta$$
$$= \delta \left[\tfrac{9}{10}\eta^{10/9} - \tfrac{9}{11}\eta^{11/9}\right]_0^1 = \tfrac{9}{110}\delta.$$

(b) The momentum integral equation (3.24) gives

$$\frac{9}{110}\frac{d\delta}{dx} = \frac{\tau_0}{\rho U^2} = \frac{0.0145}{(U\delta/\nu)^{1/5}}, \quad \text{or}$$
$$\delta^{1/5}\frac{d\delta}{dx} = \frac{110}{9} \times \frac{0.0145}{(U/\nu)^{1/5}}.$$

Integration gives (since $\delta = 0$ when $x = 0$)

$$\tfrac{5}{6}\delta^{6/5} = \frac{110}{9} \times \frac{0.0145x}{(U/\nu)^{1/5}}, \qquad \text{or}$$

$$\delta = \left(\frac{6}{5} \times \frac{110}{9} \times \frac{0.0145x}{(U/\nu)^{1/5}}\right)^{5/6}, \qquad \text{that is,}$$

$$\frac{\delta}{x} = \frac{0.275}{(Ux/\nu)^{1/6}}.$$

Hence

$$\tau_0 = \frac{0.0145\rho U^2}{(U\delta/\nu)^{1/5}} = \frac{0.0145\rho U^2}{(U/\nu)^{1/5}} \left(\frac{0.275x}{(Ux/\nu)^{1/6}}\right)^{-1/5}$$

$$= \frac{0.0188\rho U^2}{(Ux/\nu)^{1/6}}.$$

The total skin friction drag per unit breadth on a plate of length L is given by

$$F_L = \int_0^L \tau_0 \, dx = \frac{0.0188\rho U^2}{(U/\nu)^{1/6}} \int_0^L x^{-1/6} \, dx$$

$$= \frac{0.0188\rho U^2}{(U/\nu)^{1/6}} \times \tfrac{6}{5}L^{5/6} = \frac{0.0225\rho U^2 L}{(UL/\nu)^{1/6}}.$$

(c) With $\nu = \mu/\rho = 1.5 \times 10^{-5} \, \mathrm{m^2 \, s^{-1}}$, the Reynolds number is, as in Solution 3.7(a),

$$Re_L = \frac{UL}{\nu} = \frac{56 \times 210}{1.5 \times 10^{-5}} = 7.84 \times 10^8.$$

The total drag force for breadth $10.75\,\mathrm{m}$ is

$$10.75 F_{210} = \frac{10.75 \times 0.0225 \times 1.20 \times 56^2 \times 210}{(7.84 \times 10^8)^{1/6}}$$

$$\simeq 6.30 \times 10^3 \, \mathrm{N}.$$

Multiplying this by the speed $56 \, \mathrm{m\,s^{-1}}$ gives the power required to overcome skin friction as $353\,\mathrm{kW}$. The maximum thickness of the boundary layer (at the back end) is

$$\delta(L) = 0.275 L (Re_L)^{-1/6}$$

$$= 0.275 \times 210 \times (7.84 \times 10^8)^{-1/6} \simeq 1.90 \, \mathrm{m}.$$

(Both values are larger than those found earlier using the one-seventh power law.)

Section 4

Solution 4.1

(a) The flow of Exercise 2.5 has $U = 1.0 \, \mathrm{m\,s^{-1}}$, $x \le 0.3 \, \mathrm{m}$ and $\nu = 1.0 \times 10^{-6} \, \mathrm{m^2\,s^{-1}}$. Hence the largest value of $Re_x = Ux/\nu$ on the plate (at the back end) is

$$Re_x = \frac{1.0 \times 0.3}{1.0 \times 10^{-6}} = 3.0 \times 10^5.$$

Thus the flow is entirely within the expected laminar flow range.

(b) The flow of Exercise 3.7 has $U = 56 \, \mathrm{m\,s^{-1}}$ and $\nu = 1.5 \times 10^{-5} \, \mathrm{m^2\,s^{-1}}$. Hence

$$Re_x = \frac{Ux}{\nu} = \frac{56x}{1.5 \times 10^{-5}} \simeq 3.73 \times 10^6 x.$$

If transition occurs at $Re_x = 5 \times 10^5$, then the transition point is at

$$x = \frac{5 \times 10^5}{3.73 \times 10^6} \simeq 0.134 \, \mathrm{m} = 13.4 \, \mathrm{cm}.$$

(This is a tiny fraction of the entire $(210\,\mathrm{m})$ length of the train; so the assumption of turbulent flow throughout is a very reasonable one.)

Solution 4.2

We have

$$[\tau_0] = (\mathrm{M\,L\,T^{-2}})\,\mathrm{L}^{-2} = \mathrm{M\,L^{-1}\,T^{-2}},$$

$$[\rho] = \mathrm{M\,L^{-3}}, \qquad [\mu] = \mathrm{M\,L^{-1}\,T^{-1}},$$

$$[\nu] = \frac{[\mu]}{[\rho]} = \frac{\mathrm{M\,L^{-1}\,T^{-1}}}{\mathrm{M\,L^{-3}}} = \mathrm{L^2\,T^{-1}},$$

so that

$$[u_\tau^2] = \frac{[\tau_0]}{[\rho]} = \frac{\mathrm{M\,L^{-1}\,T^{-2}}}{\mathrm{M\,L^{-3}}} = \mathrm{L^2\,T^{-2}} = (\mathrm{L\,T^{-1}})^2,$$

and

$$[\delta_\nu] = \frac{[\nu]}{[u_\tau]} = \frac{\mathrm{L^2\,T^{-1}}}{\mathrm{L\,T^{-1}}} = \mathrm{L}.$$

Solution 4.3

If $\tau = \tau_0 (1 - y/\delta)$ and $l_m = \kappa y (1 - y/\delta)^{1/2}$, then Equation (3.28) gives

$$\tau_0 \left(1 - \frac{y}{\delta}\right) = \rho \kappa^2 y^2 \left(1 - \frac{y}{\delta}\right) \left(\frac{\partial u}{\partial y}\right)^2,$$

which after division through by $1 - y/\delta$ leads to Equation (4.5).

Solution 4.4

(a) Since $c_f = \tau_0/(\tfrac{1}{2}\rho U^2) = 0.0045$, we have

$$\tau_0 = \tfrac{1}{2} c_f \rho U^2 = \tfrac{1}{2} \times 0.0045 \times 1000 \times 1^2 = 2.25 \, \mathrm{N\,m^{-2}}.$$

(b) The friction velocity is

$$u_\tau = \sqrt{\frac{\tau_0}{\rho}} = \sqrt{\frac{2.25}{1000}} \simeq 0.0474 \, \mathrm{m\,s^{-1}},$$

and the viscous length scale is

$$\delta_\nu = \frac{\nu}{u_\tau} \simeq \frac{1.0 \times 10^{-6}}{0.0474} \simeq 2.11 \times 10^{-5} \, \mathrm{m} \, (\simeq 0.02 \, \mathrm{mm}).$$

(c) Hence

$$5\delta_\nu \simeq 1.05 \times 10^{-4} \, \mathrm{m} \, (\simeq 0.10 \, \mathrm{mm}) \quad \text{and}$$

$$30\delta_\nu \simeq 6.32 \times 10^{-4} \, \mathrm{m} \, (\simeq 0.63 \, \mathrm{mm}).$$

(d) Putting $u = u_c$ into Equation (4.9), together with $y = 0.05 \, \mathrm{m}$ (the radius a of the pipe), and using the value of u_τ from part (b), we have

$$u_c = u_\tau \left(5.75 \log_{10}\left(\frac{u_\tau a}{\nu}\right) + 5.5\right)$$

$$\simeq 0.0474 \left(5.75 \log_{10}\left(0.0474 \times 0.05 \times 10^6\right) + 5.5\right)$$

$$\simeq 1.18 \, \mathrm{m\,s^{-1}}.$$

(e) Similarly, with $\delta_\nu = \nu/u_\tau$,

$$u(30\delta_\nu) = u_\tau \left(5.75 \log_{10}(30) + 5.5\right)$$

$$\simeq 0.664 \, \mathrm{m\,s^{-1}}.$$

For $y = 5\delta_\nu$, Equation (4.9) does not apply. Instead we use Equation (4.3), which gives

$$u(5\delta_\nu) = 5u_\tau \simeq 0.237 \, \mathrm{m\,s^{-1}}.$$

Hence

$$\frac{u(5\delta_\nu)}{u_c} = 20.1\% \qquad \text{and} \qquad \frac{u(30\delta_\nu)}{u_c} = 56.2\%.$$

Solution 4.5

(a) For the situation described in Exercise 4.4, the Reynolds number is
$$Re = \frac{Ud}{\nu} = \frac{1.0 \times 0.1}{1.0 \times 10^{-6}} = 1 \times 10^5.$$
According to Figure 4.4 the corresponding value of λ is about 0.018, leading to $c_f = \frac{1}{4}\lambda \simeq 0.0045$, as given in Exercise 4.4.

(b) Equation (4.19) in this case is
$$p_{n+1} = \left[2.0 \log_{10}(10^5 p_n) - 0.80\right]^{-1}$$
$$= \left[2.0 \log_{10} p_n + 9.20\right]^{-1}.$$
If $\lambda_0 = 0.018$ and $p_0 = \sqrt{\lambda_0} \simeq 0.134$, then
$$p_1 = \left[2.0 \log_{10}(0.134) + 9.20\right]^{-1} = 0.134,$$
which is the same as p_0 to 3 decimal places. This again confirms that $c_f = 0.0045$ is the appropriate choice for Exercise 4.4.

Solution 4.6

The mean flow rate is
$$U = \frac{0.06}{\pi \times (0.1)^2} \simeq 1.91 \,\mathrm{m\,s^{-1}}.$$
So the Reynolds number is
$$Re = \frac{Ud}{\nu} \simeq \frac{1.91 \times 0.2}{1.0 \times 10^{-6}} \simeq 3.82 \times 10^5.$$
For this value of Re, Figure 4.4 suggests that $\lambda \simeq 0.014$. Using the iteration formula (4.19) with $Re = 3.82 \times 10^5$ and $p_0 = \sqrt{0.014} \simeq 0.118$ gives $p_2 = p_3 = 0.1176$ to 4 decimal places, corresponding to $\lambda = (0.1176)^2 \simeq 0.0138$.

The Darcy–Weisbach equation (4.20) then gives
$$-\frac{dp}{dx} = \frac{\lambda \rho U^2}{2d} = \frac{0.0138 \times 1000 \times (1.91)^2}{2 \times 0.2}$$
$$\simeq 126 \,\mathrm{Pa\,m^{-1}}.$$

Over 10 m of pipe, the pressure drop will therefore need to be 1260 Pa. (This corresponds to a 'head loss' Δh given by $\Delta p = \rho g \Delta h$, that is, $\Delta h = 1260/(1000 \times 9.81) \simeq 0.128$ m.)

Solution 4.7

(a) Assuming rough turbulent flow, we apply Equation (4.23) in the form
$$\frac{u}{u_\tau} = 2.50 \ln \left(\frac{30y}{k_s}\right).$$
We have $y = 4$ at depth 1 m and $y = 1$ at depth 4 m; so
$$\frac{u(4)}{u(1)} = \frac{\ln(120/k_s)}{\ln(30/k_s)} = \frac{1.2}{0.95} = \frac{24}{19}.$$
Hence
$$19 \left(\ln 120 - \ln k_s\right) = 24 \left(\ln 30 - \ln k_s\right), \qquad \text{or}$$
$$5 \ln k_s = 24 \ln 30 - 19 \ln 120$$
$$= \ln\left(\frac{30^{24}}{120^{19}}\right) = \ln\left(30^5 \times 4^{-19}\right).$$
It follows that
$$k_s^5 = 30^5 \times 4^{-19}, \qquad \text{or}$$
$$k_s = 30 \times 4^{-19/5} \simeq 0.1546 \,\mathrm{m}.$$

(Other methods of solution are possible here, including trial and error.)

The friction velocity u_τ is given by
$$\frac{u(1)}{u_\tau} = 2.50 \ln \left(\frac{30}{k_s}\right) \simeq 13.17,$$
from which
$$u_\tau \simeq \frac{0.95}{13.17} \simeq 0.0721 \,\mathrm{m\,s^{-1}}.$$
At the surface ($y = 5$), the flow speed is
$$2.50 u_\tau \ln \left(\frac{150}{k_s}\right) \simeq 1.24 \,\mathrm{m\,s^{-1}}.$$

(b) Since
$$\frac{u_\tau k_s}{\nu} \simeq \frac{0.0721 \times 0.1546}{1.0 \times 10^{-6}} \simeq 1.1 \times 10^4,$$
which is greater than 70, the flow is rough as assumed.

Solution 4.8

(a) Equation (4.21) is
$$\frac{u}{u_\tau} = A \ln \left(\frac{y}{k_s}\right) + D,$$
so that the mean velocity of the flow is
$$U = \frac{u_\tau}{h} \int_0^h \left(A \ln \left(\frac{y}{k_s}\right) + D\right) dy.$$
Since $\int \ln(ay)\, dy = y\left(\ln(ay) - 1\right)$, from integration by parts, this becomes
$$U = \frac{u_\tau}{h} \left[Ay \left(\ln \left(\frac{y}{k_s}\right) - 1\right) + Dy\right]_0^h$$
$$= u_\tau \left[A \left(\ln \left(\frac{h}{k_s}\right) - 1\right) + D\right].$$

(b) The value of y at which $u = U$ is given by
$$A \ln \left(\frac{y}{k_s}\right) + D = A \left(\ln \left(\frac{h}{k_s}\right) - 1\right) + D,$$
that is,
$$\ln \left(\frac{y}{k_s}\right) = \ln \left(\frac{h}{k_s}\right) - 1, \qquad \text{or} \qquad \ln \left(\frac{y}{h}\right) = -1.$$
It follows that
$$\frac{y}{h} = e^{-1} \qquad \text{or} \qquad y = e^{-1}h \simeq 0.368\,h.$$

(c) From part (a), with $A = 2.50$, $D = 8.5$, we have
$$\frac{U}{u_\tau} = 2.50 \ln \left(\frac{h}{k_s}\right) + 6.0.$$
For $h = 2.5$ m, $U = 1.2\,\mathrm{m\,s^{-1}}$, $k_s = 0.2$ m, it follows that
$$\frac{1.2}{u_\tau} = 2.50 \ln \left(\frac{2.5}{0.2}\right) + 6.0 \simeq 12.3,$$
or $u_\tau = 0.0974\,\mathrm{m\,s^{-1}}$. The shear stress at the bed is
$$\tau_0 = \rho u_\tau^2 \simeq 9.50 \,\mathrm{N\,m^{-2}}.$$

Solution 4.9

The mean velocity is
$$U = \frac{0.157}{\pi(0.125)^2} \simeq 3.20 \,\mathrm{m\,s^{-1}}.$$
Hence the Reynolds number is
$$Re = \frac{Ud}{\nu} \simeq \frac{3.20 \times 0.25}{1.0 \times 10^{-6}} \simeq 8.0 \times 10^5.$$

For this value of Re and $k_s/d = 0.25/250 = 10^{-3}$, the Moody diagram (Figure 4.9) gives $\lambda \simeq 0.020$. Equation (4.28) with $p_0 = \sqrt{0.020} \simeq 0.1414$ gives $p_1 = p_2 = 0.1415$, for which $\lambda = p^2 \simeq 0.0200$. (Note that, since

$$u_\tau = U\sqrt{\tfrac{1}{2}c_f} = U\sqrt{\tfrac{1}{8}\lambda} = 0.16\,\mathrm{m\,s^{-1}},$$

we have $k_s u_\tau/\nu = 40$ here. This is below the fully rough range, and consequently Equation (4.26) does not give as accurate an answer as the Colebrook–White equation.)

Solution 4.10

(a) Since $c_f = \tfrac{1}{4}\lambda = \tau_0/(\tfrac{1}{2}\rho U^2)$, the shear stress at the wall is

$$\tau_0 = \tfrac{1}{8} \times 0.020 \times 1000 \times 8^2 = 160\,\mathrm{N\,m^{-2}}.$$

The friction velocity is

$$u_\tau = \sqrt{\frac{\tau_0}{\rho}} = \sqrt{\frac{160}{1000}} = 0.4\,\mathrm{m\,s^{-1}}.$$

(b) Since

$$Re = \frac{Ud}{\nu} = \frac{8.0 \times 0.25}{1.0 \times 10^{-6}} = 2.0 \times 10^6 > 2300,$$

the flow is turbulent. Since

$$\frac{u_\tau k_s}{\nu} = \frac{0.4 \times 0.25 \times 10^{-3}}{1.0 \times 10^{-6}} = 100 > 70,$$

the flow is rough.

From Equation (4.23), the maximum velocity u_c (at $y = a = 0.125$) is

$$u_c = u_\tau\left(5.75\log_{10}\left(\frac{a}{k_s}\right) + 8.5\right)$$

$$= 0.4\left(5.75\log_{10}\left(\frac{0.125}{0.25 \times 10^{-3}}\right) + 8.5\right)$$

$$\simeq 9.61\,\mathrm{m\,s^{-1}}.$$

Hence, with $a = 0.125\,\mathrm{m}$, we have

$$\frac{u}{u_c} = \frac{0.4}{9.61}\left(5.75\log_{10}\left(\frac{y}{0.25 \times 10^{-3}}\right) + 8.5\right)$$

$$= 0.239\log_{10}\left(\frac{500y}{a}\right) + 0.354$$

$$= 0.239\log_{10}\left(\frac{y}{a}\right) + 1.00.$$

The velocity profiles are on the graph in part (d).

(c) Reducing the volume flow rate by a factor of 100 means that now $U = 0.08\,\mathrm{m\,s^{-1}}$. The Reynolds number is now

$$Re = \frac{Ud}{\nu} = \frac{0.08 \times 0.25}{1.0 \times 10^{-6}} = 2.0 \times 10^4 > 2300,$$

and so the flow is still turbulent. Since $k_s/d = 0.25/250 = 0.001$, the Moody diagram (Figure 4.9) gives $\lambda \simeq 0.028$. The iteration formula (4.28), with $p_0 = \sqrt{0.028} \simeq 0.167$ gives $p_1 = p_2 = 0.1672$, so $\lambda = (0.1672)^2 \simeq 0.02795$.

The shear stress at the wall is

$$\tau_0 = \tfrac{1}{8} \times 0.02795 \times 1000 \times (0.08)^2$$

$$\simeq 2.236 \times 10^{-2}\,\mathrm{N\,m^{-2}},$$

and the friction velocity is

$$u_\tau = \sqrt{\frac{\tau_0}{\rho}} = \sqrt{\frac{2.236 \times 10^{-2}}{1000}} \simeq 4.73 \times 10^{-3}\,\mathrm{m\,s^{-1}}.$$

Since

$$\frac{u_\tau k_s}{\nu} = \frac{4.73 \times 10^{-3} \times 0.25 \times 10^{-3}}{1.0 \times 10^{-6}} \simeq 1.18 < 5,$$

the turbulent flow is smooth, and so Equation (4.9) applies. The velocity at the centre is

$$u_c = u_\tau\left(5.75\log_{10}\left(\frac{u_\tau a}{\nu}\right) + 5.5\right)$$

$$= 4.73 \times 10^{-3}\left(5.75\log_{10}\left(\frac{4.73 \times 10^{-3} \times 0.125}{1.0 \times 10^{-6}}\right) + 5.5\right)$$

$$\simeq 0.1014\,\mathrm{m\,s^{-1}},$$

so that

$$\frac{u}{u_c} = \frac{4.73 \times 10^{-3}}{0.1014}\left(5.75\log_{10}\left(\frac{4.73 \times 10^{-3}y}{1.0 \times 10^{-6}}\right) + 5.5\right)$$

$$= 0.0466\left(5.75\log_{10}\left(\frac{591y}{a}\right) + 5.5\right)$$

$$= 0.268\log_{10}\left(\frac{y}{a}\right) + 1.00.$$

This velocity profile is plotted on the graph in part (d).

(d) Reducing the volume flow rate by a further factor of 20 means that now $U = 0.004\,\mathrm{m\,s^{-1}}$. Since

$$Re = \frac{Ud}{\nu} = \frac{0.004 \times 0.25}{1.0 \times 10^{-6}} = 1000 < 2300,$$

this is laminar flow. Now

$$\lambda = 4c_f = \frac{64}{Re} = 0.064,$$

from the Moody diagram or from Equation (2.31). The shear stress at the wall is

$$\tau_0 = \tfrac{1}{8} \times 0.064 \times 1000 \times (0.004)^2 \simeq 1.28 \times 10^{-4}\,\mathrm{N\,m^{-2}}.$$

The velocity is given in this laminar case (see before Exercise 2.7 here and Equation (2.13) of *Unit 8*) by

$$u(r) = \frac{C}{4\mu}(a^2 - r^2), \qquad \text{so that}$$

$$u_c = \frac{Ca^2}{4\mu} \qquad \text{and} \qquad \frac{u(r)}{u_c} = 1 - \frac{r^2}{a^2}.$$

In terms of $y = a - r$, this is

$$\frac{u}{u_c} = \frac{y}{a}\left(2 - \frac{y}{a}\right),$$

whose profile is plotted below.

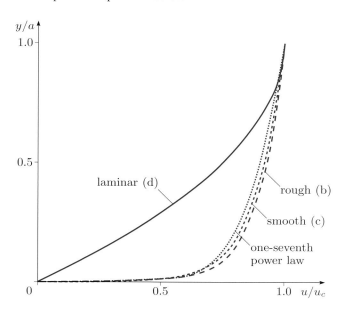

Index